# If it happens to you

*To Glen Colgan, born an angel, 12 January 1990;*
*to all babies who will never see the light of day;*
*and to*
*Tanya-Samantha, 9 April 1984*

# If it happens to you
## Miscarriage and stillbirth –
## A human insight

*Karina Colgan*

First published in 1994 by
A. & A. Farmar
Beech House
78 Ranelagh Village
Dublin 6

ISBN 0 9509295 6 5

British Library Cataloguing in Publication Data
A CIP catalogue record for this book is available from the British Library

Typeset in Ireland by Phototype-Set Ltd
Printed in Ireland by Colour Books
Cover design by Syd Bluett
Cover photograph by Hugh MacConville

# Contents

# Acknowledgements

I would like to thank all the people who so generously gave their time to contribute in some way to this book; all the mothers and fathers who shared their experiences with me, the Miscarriage Association of Ireland, Imelda Keogh and Fr Bryan Nolan, Ronnie Fay, The Travellers' Association, Barry O'Sullivan, and Dr Peter Boylan for writing the Foreword.

I would like to give special thanks to my publisher, Anna Farmar, for believing in me, to my mother for her constant encouragement and advice (not to mention unlimited babysitting!), to my children Karl and Sarah for being so good, and finally to my husband, Gerry, without whose love and support this book would not have been possible.

# Preface

When I was six months pregnant an ultrasound revealed that the baby I was carrying was dying and in all probability would be stillborn.

I was devastated. I was immediately thrown into an unknown world full of things I didn't really understand. My questions seemed inappropriate. I was fully informed at all times about what was going to happen from a medical point of view, but what I really wanted to know was – what was going to happen to me?

I knew that I was going to give birth to a dead baby, but I didn't know how to react. There were no guidelines, no code of ethics to go by. I needed to know if what I was feeling was normal, if my reactions were comparable to those of other women in my situation. I had a need to find out everything I could about stillbirth, not from a medical viewpoint, but from the point of view of ordinary women like me.

I searched everywhere for a book that I could relate to but I was unable to find one. All I could find were books full of medical terms that I was not familiar with or written for people who had already gone through the experience of miscarriage or stillbirth. A lot of my questions went unanswered. Six weeks later I gave birth to my stillborn son.

In the weeks before the birth, I went around in a state of utter confusion. I had been told what would happen and yet I still didn't know what to expect. My emotions were in turmoil and I frequently did things that were totally out of character. I experienced feelings that were alien to me. I was not prepared for this, it was something that happened to 'somebody else'. After getting past the dreaded first twelve weeks, I had been confident of a healthy baby. I had never once thought about something going wrong and when it did, I found it very difficult to accept and come to terms with.

I vowed that some day, when I felt I was ready, I would sit down and write the book that I had needed, but that didn't exist, a book that would answer my questions, a book that would help those who came into contact with miscarriage and stillbirth to understand what was happening, a book that would give an insight on a personal level.

From my own experience and that of the many people I spoke to in the course of writing this book, it is clear that there is still room for progress in some areas. People need to have a better understanding of the needs and wishes of women and men who have suffered the loss of their child at *any* stage of the pregnancy.

This book will not take away the pain and loss of losing a baby. It will, however, answer some of the many questions that people want to ask, but don't. I hope that it will contribute to a better understanding of what a miscarriage or a stillbirth means to the people involved, and will give some solace to those who have had to endure such a loss – there is light at the end of the tunnel.

# Foreword

The emotional impact of miscarriage and stillbirth has been widely recognised only in the past ten years or so. The couple's response to the loss varies widely – from utter despair to apparently little effect. For many women, losing a baby in this way can be a very lonely time when every other woman seems either to be pregnant or with a young baby; for men the sense of loss may present a major challenge to their masculinity and sense of worth.

About 15 per cent of recognised pregnancies end in miscarriage and about 1 per cent of babies are either stillborn or die soon after birth. The cause of miscarriage is rarely clearly identified. It is usually associated with some problem which exists from conception and is almost never caused by something the mother has done. At the other end of pregnancy, one-third of babies who are stillborn or who die soon after birth have conditions which cannot be cured; another one-third of deaths are associated with very premature birth and the remainder are either associated with pregnancy complications or are unexplained.

The emotional dimension of pregnancy loss has become more widely recognised among doctors, nurses and social workers in recent years. This greater understanding has resulted in the establishment of miscarriage clinics in a number of hospitals and of training programmes for professionals who care for the couple involved at whatever stage of pregnancy.

Parents can be assured that counselling and support in coming to terms with the loss and in making difficult decisions will be provided at every step along the way from first diagnosis, through delivery, and afterwards for as long as necessary. It is also well recognised, however, that one's ability to absorb information at a time of grief is limited by the associated stress.

This is one of the areas where Karina Colgan's book makes a most valuable contribution: it allows readers to share, in their own time, the experiences of others who have gone through a similiar loss. The book is very welcome and indeed necessary as there appears to be no other work approaching the subject in the same way. It will help to alleviate many of the problems encountered and will assist greatly in the grieving process.

*Dr Peter Boylan*
*Master*
*National Maternity*
*Hospital*
*Holles Street, Dublin*
*January 1994*

# Miscarriage and stillbirth

When a baby dies in the womb before the stage of 24 weeks' gestation this is termed a 'miscarriage'. When a baby dies after 24 weeks' gestation and is then born this is called a 'stillbirth'. In effect, many 'late' miscarriages are stillbirths.

**Early miscarriage**
Seventy-five per cent of miscarriages occur in the first twelve weeks and one in five pregnancies result in miscarriage. Very often, a woman has a miscarriage without realising that she was pregnant. A miscarriage in the very early stages of pregnancy could be mistaken for a late or heavy period.

When a miscarriage occurs in early pregnancy, the shock, as at any stage, may be severe. The couple are often still in the process of telling everyone their good news when suddenly, without warning, their baby is gone.

It is important to remember that, although a woman may not 'look' pregnant, she feels pregnant. From the moment it is confirmed that she is pregnant, the mother begins to bond with the baby that is growing inside her and looks forward to seeing her baby's face.

From the very onset, both she and the father have hopes and dreams for their baby. They look forward to a future that will include their baby. The baby, even at this early stage, has become a part of their lives.

Many people are of the opinion that to lose a baby

in the early stages of pregnancy is something that is easily forgotten and of little importance, but this is not the case.

To miscarry at this early stage of pregnancy has a physical impact on the mother and an emotional impact on both the mother and father.

In the later stages of an 'early' miscarriage, sometimes it is necessary for the mother to have a D&C. This is an operation performed to ensure that the womb is empty. The mother has to have a general anaesthetic. This is an additional worry, especially if she has never had surgery before.

The mother experiences pain whilst miscarrying, although the intensity of this pain can vary greatly from one woman to another. Some women have described this pain as akin to 'a bad period pain', others have described it as 'excruciating'. Most are not aware of what a miscarriage entails and feel frightened by what is happening.

**Late miscarriage**
Although losing a baby before the 24th week is defined as a miscarriage, many women who lose a baby from the fourteenth week onwards find themselves in the position of having to give 'birth'.

Not every mother who has a miscarriage is able to see and hold the baby, however small. For those who can, it may be very upsetting to know that their little baby was recognised only as a miscarriage. The word 'miscarriage' takes away the vivid reality of what has happened: the death of a baby.

A miscarriage at any stage should *never* be dismissed as 'just one of those things'. A miscarriage is *always* the death of a baby. The ensuing grief of the parents must be acknowledged and support given to them.

**Stillbirth**

'Stillbirth' is the word used to describe the birth of a baby who died after reaching 24 weeks' gestation or more. In many cases, the parents are aware that their baby is dead before labour begins. The mother knows that she will have to go through labour and give birth to a dead baby. It is emotionally draining and can also be very frightening.

# Karina's story

My husband, Gerry, and I were delighted when our first child, Karl, was born in 1987. My next two pregnancies ended in miscarriage, but in the summer of 1989 we were overjoyed when it was confirmed I was pregnant again. I immediately went for my first visit to the maternity hospital and was told that the baby was due in the spring. When I got past the dreaded first three months, and the 'bump' became more obvious, I began to relax. We chose two names – 'Glen' for a boy and 'Melody' for a girl. I was convinced that the bump was a girl, and when I spoke to the baby I would tap my stomach and call 'Melody'.

As the months passed I built up quite a collection of baby paraphernalia, and by the autumn I had drawers full of vests, cardigans, Babygros and blankets. Around that time my back began to give me a lot of trouble and I was in constant pain. I was not unduly worried about this because I suffer from sciatica. However, the pain became intolerable and I decided to go to the hospital to see if anything could be done. The fact that I was pregnant meant that I couldn't take any of the usual pain-relieving tablets.

The consultant was horrified at the state I was in – I was dependent on crutches to get around – and said that he was going to admit me for complete bedrest. Initially I was opposed to this because it meant that I'd be apart from Karl, who was now two and a half years old, but in the end I agreed with Gerry that it was for the best. I was admitted that evening and decided that as I was going to be in hospital for a while, I might as well make the most of it and enjoy the rest!

Towards the end of the week I began to feel a little better and asked about going home, promising to continue bedrest there. It was decided that I could go home the following day and I was thrilled – I missed Gerry and Karl terribly.

When I woke up the following morning, I was in high spirits; my back was a lot better and I was looking forward to going home that evening. Later on that morning, I went for a routine ultrasound scan. After lunch, a nurse came to tell me that I had to go for another scan. I remember saying to her, 'It must be a very good looking baby!' When we arrived at the scan room, the doctor who looked after me throughout my pregnancy was already there. The moment I saw her, I knew that something was wrong, very wrong.

As I sat facing the doctor, I didn't realise quite how bad things were. I thought perhaps she was going to advise me that I should remain in hospital, because of my back. The doctor gently explained to me that there was something seriously wrong with the baby. She suggested that I wait until Gerry arrived, before we went any further. My first reaction was to burst into tears. I kept saying 'Melody will live, won't she?', but when the doctor didn't dispel my fears I realised that there was a chance that the baby could die. I began to panic and remember saying to the doctor that she couldn't let anything happen to my baby, I loved her too much and we wanted her so much, already she was part of our family. The doctor squeezed my arm and said that the minute Gerry arrived we were to get her paged and she would come and see us immediately.

In a daze I left the room. I went to the telephone and called Gerry. I was practically incoherent as, through my sobbing, I tried to explain to him what had happened. He told me not to worry, he was on his way. I then called my mother; again I tried to explain what had happened and she too told me to calm down, she was coming straight in.

Somehow, I managed to make my way back to the ward and as I walked through the door a hush descended on the room: the women I had been laughing and joking with less than an hour ago now averted their eyes. I returned to my bed, pulled the curtain around and sat calmly waiting for Gerry and my mother to come. Gerry arrived about twenty minutes later, and as soon as I saw him my composure went and I cried as he held me in his arms. After my mother arrived Gerry convinced me to page the doctor. I had been putting it off because there was a part of me saying, 'It's all a mistake'. I was afraid to hear what the doctor had to say. As we were waiting for her to arrive, I repeated in my head, 'I can cope with anything, God, please don't let Melody die, please don't take her away from me.'

When the doctor arrived she took all three of us to the scan room. She started by saying that she was so sorry, that this was the worst part of her job and that unless she was one hundred per cent certain of her findings, she would not put us through this. Gently she explained that our baby was seriously ill and its chance of surviving until birth were remote. Our baby was dying. As she spoke to us, the baby kicked and I remember screaming 'You are making a terrible mistake!' Gerry had to try and calm me down.

I asked the doctor how could she tell me that my baby was dying when I could feel the kicking. She told us that our baby was very, very sick and that if by some miracle it did survive until birth, it would die immediately. At the time I remember thinking she was being cruel by taking away all our hope, now I know that she was only preparing us for the inevitable.

I went home a couple of days later. I was in a daze. Everything seemed like a bad dream and I kept wishing that I could wake up and things would be back to normal. We tried to explain to Karl that the baby was very sick. We told him that the baby would be living with Holy God and that he would mind the baby for us. Although Karl was only two and a half, he understood far more than we expected. He constantly asked questions, which we encouraged. He listened intently to our answers and reasoned things out in his own mind.

As Christmas approached, I simply couldn't face it. I couldn't contemplate the thought of celebrating anything. We didn't even put up a Christmas tree. I was too upset to leave the house, it had become my prison since leaving the hospital. I couldn't bear to see anyone and sat day after day with the curtains drawn. We went to my parents' house for Christmas Day. I felt that for Karl's sake we had to have Christmas dinner. Karl opened his presents in my parents' house and they and my sister made a big fuss of him. I thought that Christmas Day would never end.

On the 30th of December, I was aware of the baby being quiet. For a few days before this, I had noticed that it hadn't been kicking quite as much as usual. I remember pleading with the baby, still convinced it was Melody, to get strong for me. I talked to the baby constantly, saying how much she was loved and wanted. I begged her not to die, I told her that I could not carry on if she died. I sang songs to her and I tried to play our game, but the baby did not respond. Since she had begun to kick, we had played a game

11

together. I would tap my stomach and say 'Melody' and in response the baby would kick the place that I had tapped. It was a game that we both enjoyed and played often.

I was so anxious not to miss a movement, I stayed up all that night and, as dawn broke on the morning of 31st December, I was still waiting. By 6 p.m. that evening, I had to face facts: it was now 24 hours since I had last felt any movement. I remember thinking to myself, 'I'd better phone the hospital, something could be wrong with the baby.'

Gerry telephoned the hospital and they advised us to come straight in. We arrived just before 8 p.m. and I was immediately brought for a scan. The nurse doing the scan was unable to find a heartbeat and kept saying to us, 'Don't worry, it's probably a fault in the machine.' As tears streamed down my face, I kept pleading with her to keep trying.

After half an hour, the nurse said that she was calling the doctor. As we waited for him to arrive (our own doctor was away) I still clung to what little hope I had. I kept saying to myself 'The machine is faulty, the doctor will be able to find the heartbeat.' The doctor arrived and introduced himself. He tried to locate the heartbeat but couldn't.

At this point, Gerry went out to my mother who was waiting outside and asked her to come in. When they came in, the doctor tried once again to find a heartbeat and again failed. Before he spoke, I knew what he was going to say. With a look of total compassion and understanding, he turned to us and said that he was so very sorry but our little baby was dead. I went numb and then started to cry, as did Gerry and my mother.

The doctor put his arm around me and asked if any of us had any questions. So many things were going around in my head, I found it difficult to think clearly. Gerry, however, did ask what would happen now. The doctor said that the best thing to do would be to induce me. He said that if I wanted, I could be admitted straight away. He recommended that we all have a cup of tea and talk about what I wanted to do. He brought us to a private room nearby, told us to take as much time as we needed and to call him when we were ready. A nurse brought us tea and asked if there was anything she could do. I felt like screaming at her, 'There is something you can do – give my baby back its life!'

As soon as we were alone, I turned to my mother and Gerry and said that I wanted to go home. I felt that I had to bring the baby home one last time. I needed time to say goodbye and to try and come to terms with what I was about to go through. I felt that once I got home, I would somehow be able to protect my baby. I needed to be able to talk to her, I needed the opportunity to tell her how sorry I was. I felt that as long as she was still inside me, to me my little baby was still alive and a part of me. I wanted to keep her there forever.

I stood looking out the window. It overlooked a busy street; everyone was jovial and hurrying to bring in the New Year. I thought to myself, 'Do they not realise that my baby is dead, how can they act as if nothing is wrong?'

We asked that the doctor be paged and as we waited for him, I could barely contain an overwhelming desire to run. There wasn't anywhere in particular I wanted to run to, I just wanted to get away from the hospital and never return. When the doctor came we explained that I wanted to go home and it was then arranged that I would return (in a few days) to be induced. We got home just before midnight and, as U2 rang in the New Year on the television, I sat in a trance.

Although it was only a couple of days before I had to return to be induced I treasured every minute and not once did I ever think that the baby inside me was dead. The minutes turned into hours and the hours to days and all too quickly it was the night before the induction. I remember wanting the night to last forever. I sat up all night just talking to the baby, talking about our family, what we all looked like, about Karl and what a great brother he would have been. I wrote a very long letter to the baby, sealed it and put it in my bag. Writing this letter helped me a great deal. I felt that it gave me the opportunity to say everything I wanted and I felt that I had given the baby something.

As dawn broke I began to get panicky. Suddenly, my resolve to be strong disappeared and I found myself not wanting to go to the hospital. I knew that once I left the house it was the beginning of the end. However, there was no way out, I had to go.

After being admitted I was put in a room near the labour ward. As Karl had been born by Caesarean section it was decided that I would be induced by tablets inserted internally rather than by a drip. These tablets were inserted every four hours. By that evening I had still not gone into labour, though I was getting minor pains. Gerry and my mother had been there all day and I suggested that they go for a bite to eat.

As I lay on the bed waiting for them to come back, the sound of the woman in the next bed really upset me. All day long, I had listened to various women in labour; Gerry and I couldn't help but hear, we were in the same room. What was hard to listen to was the nurse coming in and saying, 'Don't worry, in another couple of hours, baby will be here.' Then we would hear the father saying to the people waiting outside the labour ward, 'It's a girl' or 'It's a boy' – that really upset us both.

During the day, the hospital social worker and chaplain came to see us. The social worker, who was excellent, explained to us the various choices we had to make about the funeral after the baby was born. She also let us talk and we felt that she was one of the few people who came close to understanding what we were going through. The chaplain also gave us the opportunity to voice our fears and Gerry talked to him at length and found it a great help. Religion didn't really come into it as much as the comfort of being able to talk to another man, man-to-man. Without the social worker and chaplain we would have felt very isolated.

Gerry and Mum returned and waited with me. By 11.30 p.m., my condition was still the same, I was getting small pains but labour hadn't really started. I told Gerry and Mum to go home, they were exhausted. They didn't want to but I reasoned with them that they were going to be coming back first thing the following morning and would need to have the strength for what the day brought. Reluctantly, they left at 12.15 a.m.

The woman who had been in the bed next to me most of the evening was now screaming with pain. Her husband and mother were taking turns to sit with her and a short while later, the midwife examined her and I heard her say 'You're ready to go to the labour ward.' Shortly afterwards, her husband yelled down to her mother (who was sitting outside) 'Congratulations, Granny, it's a girl!' It was at this moment that the most awful pain racked my body.

I got a fright because it was so sudden; I had never experienced pain like it. When it didn't subside, I began to panic. The end had come and I didn't want it to. After trying to breathe in puffs, I found that the pain was getting worse. I was afraid to call for a nurse because I thought that things would happen too quickly and Gerry wouldn't get back in time. I managed to telephone my mother. She told me to get a doctor and that she would collect Gerry and come straight in. They arrived just as the nurse called for the doctor. When I saw Gerry, I begged him to make the pain stop. The midwife came in and I was examined. She explained that I was having contractions but my cervix wasn't opening. The doctor who had been attending me all day arrived. He examined me and reiterated what the midwife said. He said that the tablets I had had were only taking effect now, but because of the number I had taken, with a vengeance.

For some inexplicable reason, my cervix would not open which meant that I would continue to have excruciating pain but wouldn't be able to deliver the baby. The doctor said that he would give me an injection to stop the pain and put me to sleep. Gerry and my mother sat with me whilst this was being done. I remember saying to Gerry, 'Don't leave me.' The injection took effect almost immediately and I began to get groggy. Gerry sat by the bed until morning.

When I awoke, Gerry told me that I had slept fitfully for three hours. The social worker came to see us – she had been told of the previous night's events. She told us that she was so sorry that all this had to happen on top of everything else. I was so shattered both mentally and physically, I could barely speak. When she left, the chaplain came; he offered his sympathies and talked to us. Both he and the social worker understood the pain that Gerry was going through. So many people failed to realise that Gerry's pain was intense. He had to be strong for me and at the same time try and come to terms with all that was happening. He was very much left out of things; people seemed to forget that it was Gerry's baby too.

After the chaplain left, a senior consultant came to see us. He explained that he felt that I had been through so much the night before there was no point in putting me through it again when there was no guarantee that it would work. He said that the best thing I could do was go home and try to relax. He gave me tablets to take at home that would bring labour on, but were primarily to 'ripen' the cervix. I was very glad to be home and felt that I had been reprieved. I didn't know how long I would have at home but I was going to treasure every moment.

At home I talked a lot to my best friend, Lorraine. She had had a stillbirth some years before. (She tells her story on pages 56–62.) I got solace from talking to her and, although I am sure I brought up some sad memories, she was glad that in some way she could help. There was so much that I needed to know: I didn't know what to expect, I didn't know what my baby would look like, I didn't know anything.

The day after I came home after the failed inducement, I went into town, and subsequently all over Dublin, desperately searching for a book that would answer my questions. I wasn't able to find a book that would give me some human insight into my situation so I just had to make do with the little bits of information that I could find. Without Lorraine and her help and understanding, I would have had no idea of what to expect or that, in many respects, the birth would be quite 'normal'. During this time, and in the following weeks, I wondered about all the people who had nobody to talk to.

After searching unsuccessfully for a book, I didn't leave the house again. I spent all day at home, not bothering to get dressed and without interest in anything. I went around in a state of total helplessness, not knowing what was ahead. Every minute of every day, I wondered if I would go into labour. The tablets I had been given to 'ripen' my cervix and hopefully induce labour were still in the cupboard – I didn't take them. I wanted to prolong things as long as possible because I knew that as soon as I went into labour, it would be the beginning of the end and nothing I could do would stop it.

Gerry and I sat up night after night talking. We went through many phases, and one we both went through was a period of 'It's my fault'. I blamed myself, Gerry blamed himself. This kind of situation makes it very easy for couples to drift apart, each caught in their own thoughts and feelings of guilt. Being told that your baby is dead is so great a shock it's almost unreal. Initially, the parents absorb the news not as a couple but as a mother and father, as two individuals. The first thought is 'Why me?' Gerry and I were able to voice our fears to each other and in the end we realised that we were not to blame. Although we each dealt with the situation in our own way, we were also able to deal with it as a couple and support each other.

Every parent has a different way of dealing with their grief. Although Gerry and I grieved together, we also each grieved in our own way. I don't drink and yet, a week after coming home after the failed inducement, I put a coat on over my nightdress, and went on crutches to the off-licence. I bought a bottle of vodka, returned home, sat at the kitchen table and drank the entire bottle. (Gerry was out and Karl was with my mother.)

I did this because I was getting to the stage where I just couldn't take any more. For over a week I had been living on the edge. I couldn't find a way to be positive, I couldn't rationalize why this was happening. I just wanted to escape but I couldn't, so I thought that if I drank the bottle of vodka I would pass out, and maybe for a few short hours I could blank out the nightmare. As I sat drinking the vodka, I talked to the baby. I poured my heart out, I went through many different emotions and my last memory is thinking, 'I hope that the vodka doesn't do the baby any harm.'

Until the birth, despite being told that the baby was dead, I never gave up hope. I needed to hope, hope is what kept me going and what made me go on. As long as I could tell myself, 'Maybe there's a mistake', I felt that I had something to cling to.

When the end came, it was quick. I got up at 8 a.m. on Friday 12th January 1990. At 8.40 a.m., I got a pain. I went into the bathroom and burst into tears. I hoped against hope that it was just a 'twinge'. Even though I had had time to prepare myself for this moment and the hours to follow, I wasn't ready. I wondered how I was going to cope. How was I going to go through this and function when it was all over? I wondered about the birth: how would I react when they took the baby away?

As I sat in the bathroom, I could feel the panic rising within me. I didn't want to let go and I prayed hard to God to let me have just another couple of days with my baby. Then I got another pain, and this one was quite bad. I knew that the time had come. Desperately, I tried to compose myself. I knew that this was the last time that I would be able to speak to my baby who I felt was safe within me. I told the baby that the time had come and I had to let her go. I tried to explain that I didn't want to and that I wanted her to stay inside me forever. I told her how much I loved her and how sorry I was. I told her that if I had had a choice, I would have given her my life.

I said my own personal farewell to my baby, tried to stop crying and began to think of what I would say to Gerry. As I washed my face, I hoped that I would be able to maintain my composure in front of Karl. I took a deep breath and called Gerry. He came in and without me having to say a word, he knew. We held each other close, each of us lost in our own thoughts, then we went out and told Karl that it was time for Mammy to go to the hospital. Gerry went to phone my mother and I tried to concentrate on the questions Karl was asking me. I remember sitting in the rocking chair looking around the room and thinking that this would be the last time that I would be in it with the baby. I knew that when I came home, everything would look the same, and yet, things would never be the same.

My mother and sister arrived and so did Lorraine. Although we had all discussed this moment in depth, a veil of silence hung over the room. Nobody knew what to say and the silence was broken only by my sobs. We sat there knowing that I was in labour and that I would have to go through it and give birth and then face what would probably be the hardest thing in my life, the sight of my little baby who was dead.

When Gerry phoned the hospital to say that I had gone into labour, he asked to speak to the doctor who had treated me from the beginning. This doctor was marvellous: she went above and beyond the call of duty. She made herself available to us 24 hours a day and always answered our questions honestly, but in such a way that instead of taking away our hope, reassured us. In the past month, I had established a bond with her and felt that she understood what we were going through and in some way had become attached to our baby. She made us feel that this birth was just as important as any other and that at the end of it, we would have a son or a daughter. That morning 'our' doctor was not on duty. When I heard that, I was devastated. How could I go through all of this with a stranger? Because we had placed our trust in her, Gerry wanted to speak to her just to reassure himself. Within minutes, she was on the phone. She asked Gerry how he was and how I was. Gerry explained how worried we both were because she wasn't on duty and explained that I was in a panic. She said that she would come straight to the labour ward as soon as we arrived and that she would attend to me and deliver the baby. That took a lot off our minds. We felt now that we would have somebody we trusted and who understood in there with us.

Time was going by very quickly and I was getting contractions every six minutes. Finally, Gerry and my Mother convinced me that I should go. I took one last look around and slowly left.

In the hospital lift bringing us to the labour ward my waters broke. Luckily, we were the only people in the lift. It stopped at the labour ward and my mother went to get a nurse and a wheelchair. As the nurse wheeled me in to a room and took my details, there were looks of pity from all the nurses.

Meanwhile, Gerry had paged our doctor. After examining me she said that I was ready to give birth. I remember crying and saying that I was not ready, I couldn't go through with it. Gently she tried to explain to me that unfortunately there was nothing I could do; in a matter of a few minutes our baby would be born. Gerry held my hand as I was wheeled into a room next to the main labour ward, still close enough for us to hear everything that was going on outside.

I remember feeling numb. It was as if all of this was happening to someone else and I was only observing it. In the distance, I heard a voice saying 'Push'. That brought me back to reality. I turned to Gerry and begged him to ask the doctor to stop. I tried to explain that I couldn't go through with this. Again the doctor asked me to push. I told her that I wasn't going to push and that I wasn't giving my baby to her. But the force of Nature was stronger than me. At 13.10, against my will, my body expelled our baby. As the baby was born, I remember screaming 'No!' All of this happened within about fifteen minutes.

The instant I gave birth, I turned my face and saw a student nurse, her face contorted with a look of utter revulsion. As I tried to work out why she looked as she did, I heard the doctor say, 'It's a baby boy and he's beautiful.' Both Gerry and I cried, as did the nurses.

As the doctor carried the baby out, silently I said goodbye to the son I loved, but would never know. Gerry went out to tell my mother who was waiting outside. She came in to me and as soon as she saw me, she started to cry. She tried to regain her composure and said that she hadn't meant to cry but she too had lost her grandson.

I was given a sedative and, as we waited to go to the ward, we heard a newborn baby cry. It was the most heartbreaking sound I have ever heard. I felt so empty inside – it was as if a part of me had died. I was very mixed up and kept asking Gerry had it really all happened, did we really have a son and was he really dead. I had this terrible urge to scream and also a terrible urge to go and get Glen and run.

I was brought to the gynaecological ward and the sister came to talk to myself and Gerry. She tried to give us words of comfort but I didn't even hear her. Then came the moment I had been dreading for such a long time: seeing my darling baby. The doctor came in, carrying Glen. He was wrapped in a white blanket. She unfolded the blanket and showed us his hands, his feet, his legs, his little arms and his beautiful little face. When I saw him, my immediate reaction was one of overwhelming sadness. As I gazed at his little face, I didn't think of him as a 'dead baby', I thought of him as my son. I was so engrossed with him, it took some time for me to realise that he was actually dead. All my dread of being afraid of him vanished. It was such a relief to see him and I wondered how I could ever have imagined that I could be afraid of the baby I gave birth to.

Although I had worried about what he would look like after being dead for so long, my fears were not realised. It was only later, looking at his photographs, that I was able to see his face as it really was and the fact that he didn't look like a newborn baby. When I looked at Glen I saw my baby and to me he looked perfect. I was oblivious of the fact that he did not look like a new baby should. Glen's abnormalities were on the inside so he looked fairly normal on the outside. However, the back of his head was slightly enlarged, his skin had peeled from above his right eye and his entire body had a general waterlogged look. Not all stillborn babies look as Glen did.

The doctor asked me if I would like to hold him, but I couldn't. I was too upset and wasn't sure if I would be able to give him back to her. I needed time to come to terms with everything. I still couldn't believe that my little baby boy would never cry, never smile and never even see my face. It was too much to bear.

I asked Gerry and Mum to leave me alone for a few minutes. I learned later that, when they left the room, Gerry broke down completely. He wept bitterly for the son he, too, had lost. Whilst they were gone, the doctor returned and asked me if I would sign a consent form for a post-mortem to be done. She left it with me and said that she would be back shortly. I sat there in a daze. One half of me was saying, 'He's gone through enough, let him rest in peace.' The other half was saying, 'If they can find anything that might help even one other baby, then his death will not have been in vain.' It took only a couple of minutes for me to decide that I should consent.

Gerry and Mum returned and my sister arrived. Gerry took her to see Glen and when she returned, although red-eyed, she said that he was beautiful and that she was glad that she had had the chance to meet him. Two of Gerry's sisters came in that evening and we took them down to the room made available to us for letting our families say goodbye to Glen.

It was a day of tears and pain and yet in some ways I felt as if I was far removed from it all. It was only when Gerry left at 11.30 p.m. that I began to think. I thought about Glen lying all alone in some cold, dark room and I began to cry. Although I had taken a sleeping tablet, I didn't sleep that night. I lay there thinking about Glen and listening to the various sounds echoing around the hospital. By the time Gerry arrived the next morning I was exhausted but ready to go and hold my son. As we were going to the morgue a feeling of intense fear swept over me. I pictured Glen lying on a slab and I began to panic. I asked Gerry to hold on for a moment before we went any further.

The scene that greeted us when we went inside the morgue couldn't have been further from what I had envisaged. There was a Moses basket on a table with flowers at its head and foot. There was a small table beside the basket with a beautiful arrangement of flowers on it. At the top of the Moses basket there were two tall candlesticks with candles burning brightly in each. It took me a minute to take this scene in. Although I could see the Moses basket, I couldn't see into it. The nurse who had accompanied us asked me if I would like to go nearer, so that I could see Glen.

Slowly I took a step towards the Moses basket and, as I did so, I could see the top of the baby's head. I took another step and saw his little face. It was then and only then that everything that had happened became a reality. I went over to the the basket and looked in. Glen was lying there as if he were asleep. The nurse asked me if I would like to hold him and I said that I would. I was crying so much, I was afraid that I would let him fall. Gently the nurse took Glen out of the basket and placed him in my arms. I will never forget that moment, it was the moment when time stood still.

The nurse left the room, to give us some time alone with our son. As I held Glen, the thing that struck me more than anything else was how cold he was. Even through the layers of blankets, I could still feel the coldness of his body. We stayed there for a long time, looking at him, touching him and taking photographs of him. We took about two dozen pictures and when the nurse returned, she took a photograph of both of us with Glen. When Gerry suggested that we say goodbye to Glen, I could not. I kept asking him for 'Just another minute'. I felt that this was going to be the last time I would be able to hold Glen and talk to him. These last few minutes were so very precious. Oblivious to any other person in the room, I clutched Glen and tried to tell him how much I loved him and how much I was going to miss him. I only had these few minutes to absorb everything about him and I put a lifetime's love into them. For just a moment, as I closed my eyes and held him close, I concentrated on remembering exactly how he felt. Silently, as I took my final look at my son, I memorised every detail. Before I handed Glen to Gerry, I wiped my tears from his little cheek and gently kissed him goodbye. Gerry wept as he said goodbye to his son.

I was like a zombie when I got home later that day. I kept feeling as if I had forgotten something, as if something was missing and then I'd remember that my little baby boy would never come home. I got very upset later on that night and wanted to go back to the hospital with blankets for Glen, in case he was cold. Eventually I calmed down and from a mixture of exhaustion and sleeping tablets I slept fitfully for a few hours.

I wanted to go back to see Glen the following day, but Gerry said that it wasn't a good idea. He told me to remember Glen as I last saw him. The rest of the day passed in a haze, I didn't go out and I didn't want to see anybody. The next day was the day of the Mass. I bought a card to put into the coffin with Glen. It was beautiful. It was for a new baby but the verse was what I wanted. Called 'God's masterpiece, a baby boy', it was a little booklet that described how special a baby boy was. I bought two – one for Glen and one to keep.

I had been up most of the night, trying to decide what to put into the coffin with Glen. In the end, I decided on the following things: the card, the letter I had written to him, a teddy bear and some photographs. In happier times when I was just a few months pregnant, I saw a little yellow teddy; it had a big smile and I decided to buy my baby its first toy. I spent a long time selecting the photographs. In the end I chose five: one of me, one of Gerry, one of Karl, one of my mother and one of our home. I felt that by putting these things in the coffin Glen would in some way know us and would know that he was not alone.

Gerry also put something special in. He's a songwriter and he took the strap off his guitar to give to Glen. This meant a lot to him and he felt that he had given his son something that was a part of him.

My mother made a beautiful robe for Glen to be dressed and buried in. She said that she was very happy to do it because she felt that it was the only thing she would ever be able to do for her little grandson.

The car collected us at 4.30 p.m. and we arrived at the morgue shortly before 5 p.m. I had all the things I wanted to put in the coffin with me. As we went into the morgue, the doctor called Gerry aside and explained that the coffin had been closed and that it would be best to leave it this way. He said that if Gerry really wanted him to open it he would, but felt that it wouldn't be a good idea. The doctor assured us that he would personally put the things we had brought for Glen into the coffin himself. He told us that my mother had been there earlier with the clothes for Glen; the coffin had already been closed, but he had opened it and dressed Glen in the clothes my mother had brought.

Many members of our families came to the morgue, but to this day I have no memory of who was there. All I saw was the coffin. It was white and a beam of light was shining on the name plate. As the priest – the priest who had married us – said prayers, my eyes were fixed on the coffin. I read the nameplate over and over; Glen Colgan, Died 12th January 1990. I kept thinking that my little baby was inside that tiny coffin and that I would never see him again. I looked at his photograph on top of the coffin and thought how it should have been. I sat there remembering what his hands looked like, how small his little legs were and how very beautiful he was.

I don't really remember much of that night. I took a double dose of sleeping tablets and slept until 5 a.m. When I got up, I went into the sitting room and just sat there looking at the photographs of Glen. I was glad that I had them; my mother had had them developed as soon as we had finished taking them in the hospital. I held the photograph of the scan that had confirmed that Glen was dying. It is a photograph I treasure because it is the only one of him when he was alive.

We arrived at the mortuary at 10.15 a.m. The priest said a few prayers and we had a minute's silence to say our own prayer. After one final prayer, it was time to go. As I stood up, I could feel my legs giving. I sat down again and tried to compose myself. When I was ready to go, Gerry lifted Glen's coffin and carried it to the car. I carried the flowers. We got into the car and Gerry and I placed the coffin across our knees.

As the car turned into the cemetery I began to panic. I clutched the coffin and begged Gerry not to go through with it. I pleaded with him not to get out of the car, I begged him not to take my son away from me. He explained to me that we had to say goodbye. He told me that he too was hurting and that this was the worst moment in his life. He said that Glen was watching over us and that we had to be strong and let go.

As Gerry handed the coffin over, I said my final goodbye. As the coffin was lowered, I became hysterical. I have a vague recollection of being carried back to the car. On the way home, I remember looking out the window. The everyday hustle and bustle of life was going on as normal and I remember thinking, 'How can this be happening? Don't people know what's happened?' But, of course, life has to go on.

We spent the rest of the day talking. Now that it was finally over, we had to begin to start accepting what had happened.

I grieved for Glen as I have never grieved before. I felt that I had somehow failed in my duty as a mother, and it took me a long time to accept that nothing I could have done would have changed things. I didn't leave the house for almost three weeks after the funeral. I lost a lot of weight. My mother finally got me eating again. Day after day she would come and try and get me to eat. One day, she made me a tomato sandwich and said to me if I wouldn't eat it for myself, would I eat it for her. That was the first step in my road to recovery.

What really made me take a good look at myself was Karl. Although he was only two and a half, he was aware that his little brother had died. One day, three weeks after the funeral, he came over to me and asked me why I didn't love him any more. I couldn't believe that he had said this. I took him in my arms and told him that I loved him more than anything in the whole wide world and that he was my special boy. I told him how sorry I was for not paying much attention to him and for not being there for him. I tried to explain that Mammy and Daddy were very sad because Glen had died. He gave me a big hug and said 'Now Mammy, you are all better.' He told me that he would mind me. I reminded myself that I had a family to think about and that it was time to wake up.

After giving Karl a kiss and hug, I stood up. I pulled the curtains and decided to clean the place from top to bottom. For the first time in a long long time, I made dinner. When Gerry got home that night, the look on his face is something I will never forget. I could almost see the worry leave his mind and it was then I realised all I had put him through.

I devoted any spare time I had to trying to find out what had been wrong with Glen and why he had died. I wrote to the Royal College of Surgeons and received a lot of information from a professor there. When the results of the autopsy were received by the hospital, we went to see the doctor who had looked after us. She went through the autopsy paragraph by paragraph and answered our questions. We were with her for over an hour and she gave us a copy of the autopsy report. Before we left, the doctor told us not to hesitate to contact her if we thought of any more questions. We felt a lot better after this meeting.

When we got home, I stayed up all night reading the autopsy report. I underlined anything I didn't understand. I got solace from this report. In a strange way, it confirmed that Glen existed.

The road to recovery was long and hard. I didn't feel better overnight; it took the best part of a year to start feeling normal again. Glen's first anniversary was hard. The pain came rushing back and, as I stood at his grave, I prayed that some day we would meet again. It is said that 'Time heals all wounds': time certainly does ease the pain, but no length of time will ever take away the memory.

Standing at Glen's grave, watching his little coffin being lowered into the ground, I thought that I would never be happy again. I could not imagine laughing again or living a day when my thoughts weren't all of Glen. But the passage of time does numb the initial overwhelming grief, and as each new day dawns the awful pain slowly subsides. It takes time, a lot of time, but the day comes when you wake up and your first thought is of something other than the lost baby.

The first time this happened to me, I felt a terrible sense of guilt. I felt that I had somehow betrayed Glen's memory. Then I pulled myself together and thought about how my mind was working. I realised that I didn't have to spend twenty-four hours a day thinking about Glen to keep his memory alive. He would always live in my heart and nothing could ever take away my memory of him. He would always be a part of our lives and we could never forget him.

The feeling of loss never goes away completely. Some women in my situation want another baby straight away, others never want to have a baby again. Most women go on to have another baby when they feel that the time is right. Gerry and I discussed this matter a lot. Karl was getting older and we hadn't planned to have such an age gap between the children. I was worried sick that if I got pregnant again the same thing would happen, but after fifteen months we felt that we had to give it one last try. We both agreed that, if anything happened with another pregnancy, that would be it. I felt that after the miscarriages and Glen, the next pregnancy would be the last. Psychologically and physically, I felt I was ready.

When it was confirmed that I was pregnant, there wasn't the same excitement as before. We did not take for granted that in nine months' time we would have a baby. I was monitored very closely by the hospital and had a scan every fortnight. I had a very bad obstetric history and everyone wanted a happy ending to this pregnancy, the medical team included.

I tried to remain detached from the baby. I was afraid to get close to it, in case anything went wrong. When it began to kick, I remembered how I had played games with Glen, when I had thought of him as Melody. I talked to the baby a lot and as the pregnancy progressed, I couldn't help loving the baby that was growing inside me.

I gave up work in the middle of November and took things easy. The baby was due on Christmas Day. I had finished all the Christmas shopping by the beginning of December. I was having a scan every week now and there were no complications, a normal birth was expected. But the worry throughout the whole of the pregnancy had exhausted me, both mentally and physically.

Karl kept asking us, would this baby die, too, like baby Glen? We reassured him that this baby would be coming home. This started up a whole barrage of questions about Glen, which we answered as honestly as we could and in a way that he understood.

From the 11th of December, we were all on tenterhooks. My own bags were packed and I had a separate bag for the baby. With only a fortnight to go, I decided that I should buy some clothes for the baby. My mother and I went in to town and I shopped until I was exhausted. I bought two of everything, right down to a baby nest, one in blue and one in pink. The assistants in the shop thought it was very funny. I arranged to exchange everything in either pink or blue, once the baby had been born! When I came home that night and put all the clothes on the bed, it was hard to believe that soon my baby would be wearing them.

During Christmas week everyone was anxious. The phone never stopped ringing, and on Christmas Eve I hoped that I would be there to see Karl's face on Christmas morning. I was still there on Christmas Day. Then when Christmas Day was over, things really began to get tense. I was afraid to move out of the house in case I went into labour. My mother was with me almost twenty-four hours a day. Poor Gerry and my mother couldn't even have a drink over the whole of Christmas because I was due at any time!

The baby was still there on New Year's Eve and on Gerry's birthday on the 6th January. I went in for a scan on the 10th January and the doctor said that, if I didn't come in over the weekend myself, I would be induced on Monday. Everyone was relieved. At last there was a definite day! The strain was beginning to take its toll. When people telephoned that night, it was as if I had given birth! Everyone was looking forward to Monday.

I woke up at 4.30 a.m. on Saturday 11th January 1992 with a terrible pain. It subsided and I decided not to wake Gerry. I stayed up and about forty-five minutes later I got another pain. I knew that this was it and began to get excited. I went through all my check-lists and ticked things off. I woke Gerry at 8 a.m. and told him it was D-Day. He ran out and phoned my mother who came down at once and everyone was excited. The pain stopped and I went back to bed. At 11 a.m. I awoke with a pain and a terrible urge to go to the toilet. We left for the hospital at 1.25 p.m. and I was taken to the labour ward. I arrived there at 2.20 p.m. and at 2.38 p.m. our baby was born. It was a beautiful little girl and when she gave her first cry, I turned to Gerry and said, 'She's alive!' Gerry was crying so much the doctor asked him if he needed a valium! He ran out to my mother and when she saw him, she thought that he was coming to tell her how I was doing. When he told her that I had had a baby girl, she couldn't believe it, it had happened so fast. Mum came in to see me and the baby and started to cry as well. Everyone came in that night and started crying. It was such a happy time.

When everyone had gone and Sarah had been brought to the nursery for the night, I just lay there, wide awake. It was 1.40 a.m. and I looked out the window, up at the sky and silently wished Glen 'Happy Birthday'. He would have been two. I was very happy and I said to Glen, 'Your baby sister looks just like you.'

As we went home with our new baby we were happier than we had ever thought we would be again. It was hard to believe that it was two years almost to the day since we had left the hospital, empty-handed and desolate, never envisaging being happy again.

Sarah is almost two now and fills our lives with joy. She is a constant reminder that there is light at the end of the tunnel. We have Glen's Remembrance Blessing framed and it is surrounded by photographs of him, and of Karl and Sarah. Glen will always be a part of our family.

# My baby died:
# seven women's stories

## Hilary's story

*Hilary is married and has three children. After having two miscarriages, she started a support group, the Miscarriage Association of Ireland, for women who have suffered miscarriages and their partners.*

'Ten years ago, miscarriage was just a medical term to me – it was something that happened to other women. We lived in Belfast at that time and had two little boys, aged four and three. Now we planned to have a third baby. I became pregnant quite quickly and all was progressing as usual except that I felt very tired and sick. In July, I had some slight spotting [spots of blood] so I went to my doctor; he reassured me and told me to rest if I was worried.

By the end of July I was nineteen weeks pregnant and I went for my usual check before going on holiday. The doctor thought that I seemed a little small for dates and asked me if I had felt life. I said that I wasn't sure so he said it was sometimes hard to be sure at this stage. He told me to be certain to come back for a check-up after the holidays.

I remember very little of that holiday. I became worried about the baby, but wouldn't admit that anything could be wrong. Then I stopped feeling pregnant but kept telling myself I must be pregnant as the doctor had told me I was. I started having nightmares about the baby being deformed, or missing limbs. It was a very unreal time: I kept telling myself all would be well when we got home, the doctor would tell me the pregnancy was fine and that I had been imagining things.

At the end of August I went to my GP's surgery and as soon as he examined me his face changed. He immediately said that he was afraid that the baby had died and I should go to hospital for a scan.

I was so glad that he told me straight out. At first I found it to be a great relief. It seemed an end to all my worries: the baby was dead and that was that. Then, as the initial shock wore off on the way home, I began to cry. I couldn't believe it, how could the baby die? There seemed no reason for it.

I went in for a scan and no baby was visible on the screen. I was told to come in after the weekend for an induction. When I was in hospital waiting to be induced, a registrar told me that the scan showed I had a hydatidiform mole, a condition where the placenta grows and there is no baby. There may be a risk of malignancy with this condition so sometimes it is necessary to delay for two years before starting another pregnancy. This upset me deeply as all I wanted was to become pregnant again. I didn't want a huge gap between my children.

I lay there all that week in hospital – it took two days to induce me – worrying about this rare condition that I had. On the Wednesday, as I was in long, slow labour, all my friends in Dublin were voting in the abortion referendum, which added to my grief. I delivered later that day. I wasn't too upset as I thought there was no baby. The hospital staff were very kind and my husband stayed with me during the labour and delivery which was such a help as I couldn't have coped without him.

It took me much longer to recover from this than from the births of our two boys. I adjusted my life to take account of the fact that I must not get pregnant for two years, and I thought I was coming to terms with it when the time came for my check-up with the gynaecologist a month later.

As I lay on my back, half undressed, he informed me in a very matter-of-fact way that I hadn't had a hydatidiform mole, that there had been a baby who had died some weeks earlier and that I could start trying for a baby anytime. I was so stunned I could say nothing, then I burst into tears. I went home feeling angrier every minute and I stayed enraged for a long time. I had spent a month adjusting to what I had been told, and now it turned out not to have been true.

They had allowed me to give birth thinking there was no baby and so I never asked to see it. I felt such mistrust of doctors. All my grief focused on this mix-up and I found it hard to sleep. I kept thinking about it all the time. Finally I went back to the gynaecologist and explained my feelings. He apologised for the mistake. This did help to lay some of my feelings to rest and then I was able to grieve for my baby. It took some months before the depression lifted.

The following spring I became pregnant again, but this time a scan at eight weeks revealed that I had again miscarried. I was very upset, but this time I knew what to expect in the hospital and I recovered from it more quickly. I was pregnant again within two months and our third son, Benjamin, was born in March 1985, two years after I had first started to try for a third baby.

Writing all this down now I am surprised how vividly the feelings of despair, grief and anger have come back to me. I can still feel them although the grief of the two miscarriages has healed now. I feel sad for my family that for two years I wasn't much fun; I was either pregnant, losing a baby or recovering. Those two years seem like a big chunk out of my life, when I was just waiting for time to move on, counting the days and the months until I would have a happy, smiling baby in my arms.

Well, Benjamin was a very happy baby, almost as though he knew what we had gone through to have him. I do not regret those two years, as I feel that I have learnt so much from the experience. It inspired me to start the Miscarriage Association of Ireland so that other women could be helped at this most traumatic time of their lives.'

### Margaret's story

*Margaret, who is forty-three, has an eleven-year-old son and is now separated from her husband. In 1979, she had a miscarriage at sixteen weeks.*

'I had been married six years without children when I had a miscarriage at sixteen weeks. It was Halloween night, I'll never forget it. It was a Friday night and the Tuesday before I had been to the hospital for a routine visit. At this stage there must have been something wrong, and I think that when I was given an internal examination it didn't help.

I got pains three days later and when I phoned my own doctor, he said that I just needed to rest. I was in very bad pain and I went into the hospital at 6 p.m. They pumped me full of drugs and I wasn't really aware of what was going on. At 3 a.m. the following morning I passed something and I remember asking the doctor if I had had a miscarriage. He said to me, 'Not at all, that wasn't a miscarriage, you'll be grand in the morning.'

When I woke up the next morning I thought I was fine and didn't think that I had had a miscarriage. Then they told me that I had had a miscarriage. It was an awful shock to me that I hadn't been told the truth when it actually happened. I thought that it was such a mean thing to do, but I took it and just accepted it. I wasn't told the sex of my baby and what happened wasn't discussed with me in any way. Everybody was hush hush about it. I was put into a room on my own and sent home the following day.

I was very dizzy when I got home and three days later I had to go back into hospital for a blood transfusion. I got three pints of blood because I was so weak.

I went back to work straight away and I never really dealt with the miscarriage. I became pregnant again in 1982 and my son was born. A couple of years later my marriage broke up. The miscarriage wasn't the only reason for this, but it was one of the reasons. We never spoke about it and my mother-in-law remarked that it had never happened in her family before.

Nobody considered the miscarriage to be important, but I considered it to be a failure. I think that was how my husband considered it too and I think that the fact we didn't talk about it was bad.

Back in 1979 there was no counselling or mention of the Church, the miscarriage I had had was nothing, it was just a big blob. It was something that wasn't supposed to happen.'

Although it has been fourteen years since Margaret lost her baby, her memory of the whole experience is as vivid as the day it happened. When we spoke together Margaret asked me questions about her own baby and what would have happened to him or her and would the baby have been buried. Her questions saddened me but also angered me. They should have been answered fourteen years ago and she should have been given the support that every mother who has a miscarriage needs.

To this day Margaret wonders if her baby was a girl or boy. She had had questions to ask, but was not encouraged to do so. Back in 1979 miscarriages and stillbirths were regarded almost as non-events and were certainly not recognised as the loss of a 'baby'. It was as if such events were a reflection on the hospital and generally the policy was to get the mother in and out as quickly as possible without fuss or reference to what had happened.

Unfortunately, Margaret is not the only woman in Ireland or elsewhere who has suffered a miscarriage and has been sent home without any discussion about it. Women who have been through an experience like Margaret's, and who still wonder about their baby, could contact the hospital where the baby was born and enquire whether or not there is any record of the birth still there. If there, it is possible that the baby's sex is known and also the birthweight, length etc. People are thankfully more aware now of what is involved in the loss of a baby through miscarriage and stillbirth and most hospitals would be only too glad to try and help in any way they can.

## Helen's story

*Helen, a business manager, is twenty-eight years old and married. She miscarried her first and only baby at seventeen weeks. She told me her story eight months after she miscarried. She and her husband plan to try for a baby later this year.*

40

'Having wanted a baby, we were delighted when I got pregnant. It was due on New Year's Day and we thought what a marvellous beginning to the New Year.

Almost from the beginning I had problems.

At seven weeks I had a show [of blood] and was terribly worried. I was told that resting in bed was all I could do. Despite the bedrest, at eight weeks I was still having frequent shows. I had a scan and it confirmed that the baby's heartbeat was fine and that everything was all right.

I felt so relieved and reassured hearing this. The bleeding stopped. A couple of weeks later I attended the hospital for my ante-natal visit and everything was fine.

By mid-July I was twelve weeks pregnant and felt that, by getting through the first three months, I had reached safety. Innocently I thought if anything was going to go wrong it would happen in the first twelve weeks.

I was still getting the odd show and went to my doctor. What he said reassured me and I was convinced that everything would be okay. I went to Galway the following week and whilst there, I had a heavy show. It stopped and I felt fine. I had no morning sickness and felt 'blooming'. I was due to go for a scan at seventeen weeks.

The night before the scan I got very upset and didn't want to go to the hospital. Although at this time there was no reason for me to worry, I had the most awful feeling that something was wrong with the baby.

The next morning I was physically very sick and also very worried. When we got to the hospital there were other women waiting for a scan, and as they talked excitedly amongst themselves, I prayed that my worry was needless.

My husband came with me when I went in for my scan. As the doctor glided the sensor across my abdomen, the image of our baby appeared on the screen. As we gazed at our perfectly formed baby, the doctor asked me if I was sure of my dates. I replied that I was. I then asked him, quite calmly, if there was a problem.

He showed me the size of the baby's head and then the size that it should be. I felt really calm and asked him questions. He answered all of them honestly, which I appreciated. I was lying there for ages and the doctor looked frantic. I remember saying to him, 'It's bad news isn't it?' He replied 'It looks that way, but I would like to get a second opinion.'

At that moment, I knew. My baby was dead.

I was to have gone for a blood test after the scan and I asked the doctor if I still had to go. He said that it wasn't necessary. At this time I was very organised and was thinking rationally. I was methodically ticking things off the list I had made in my head for this hospital visit.

I got up and went to the toilet, still very calm and collected. It was only on my way back to the doctor that the awful reality of what had just happened hit me. I broke down and cried for the baby that I would never even see. My nightmare had come true.

I went back in and the doctor said that it was necessary to examine me. After this she talked to us and explained that it would be better if I went into labour naturally rather than inducing me now. However, if I didn't go into labour spontaneously within two weeks, it would be necessary to induce me.

At this stage I was really hysterical. It was arranged that I would return to the hospital three days later for another scan and a second opinion. I had the whole weekend to go through first. The doctor told me that if I had any bleeding to come in straight away.

I went home and it was as if all of this was happening to someone else. I was totally numb. All of our families were very upset but I was calm and was reassuring them. I even went out the following night. I didn't drink because I thought that if I was taken into hospital and needed an operation, alcohol in my blood might not be good. Now I know that I was in shock. It really didn't register that the baby was dead.

Over the weekend I began to get very frightened. I wanted to ask about the baby. I wanted to know would I go into labour. I was terrified and didn't know what to expect. I didn't know what was going to happen, I didn't know what the bleeding would be like, whether there would be a lot, whether it would happen all at once, how it would start. I was so frightened that I wouldn't let my husband leave my side for a single minute that whole weekend.

We returned to the hospital for the second opinion on the Monday. There were two doctors there and they confirmed what I knew. It was agreed that I should be given time to go into labour spontaneously. I was again told to come straight in if I had any bleeding.

When we left the hospital, my husband had to go to work and I didn't want to be on my own, so I went to work too. I wanted to feel normal.

Three hours later I started bleeding. My friend brought me straight to the hospital. Once there I felt safe and knew that if anything was going to happen, I was in the right place.

I didn't feel a sense of panic when I rang my husband. The bleeding had stopped and I was worried that they would send me home. The doctor felt that it would be best to perform a D&C. I was admitted and it was arranged that I would be taken to theatre the next morning. I was worried about having an operation, I had never had one before. I didn't think about why I had to have it. I didn't think of it as an operation to remove my little baby – maybe because I didn't really believe that my baby was dead.

My sister-in-law had had a baby in the same hospital the day before we were told that our baby was dead. There was great joy and jubilation and when we got the bad news, we made the decision to tell only our immediate family. We didn't want to put a damper on the new parents' happiness. However, being in the same hospital it was inevitable that my husband would bump into a member of the family who was in visiting my sister-in-law. He did and soon everyone knew.

They all came to see me and remarked how well I was coping. I felt that I was and that if I continued like this, I'd be fine. When everyone left I tried to keep occupied and put what was going to happen the next morning to the back of my mind. I was very calm.

The D&C was scheduled for 10.30 a.m. Right up to the time I went to theatre, all I was worried about was the anaesthetic. As I've said, I had never had an operation before and I was really worried about it.

When I returned from theatre and came around, I was very sick. Then suddenly, I began to feel an overwhelming sense of loss. I wanted to go home. I felt that I couldn't keep the pretence up any longer. Now that the reality of what had happened hit me, I needed time to release the grief that had been building up inside me. I needed to grieve. I felt desolate. I began to think of so many things. I had wanted a printout of the scan image of my baby, but when I said this to the family, they said that it would only upset me. I was sorry that I had listened to this advice instead of my own instinct. I regret not getting this photo. It would have shown that my baby existed.

I went home from hospital the following day. In the weeks that followed I was fine. Then it suddenly hit me and I was devastated. I grieved for the baby I had wanted so much but would never have. Grief would hit me at weird times – not when I saw other babies, but when I was just doing everyday things. The time that it hit me worst was in the weeks coming up to Christmas. I kept thinking about how things should have been and about how I would have been almost due to have the baby I had lost. I began to notice pregnant women, it seemed that everywhere I looked there was a pregnant woman.

On my due date I sat with the family watching an episode of Coronation Street. The episode being screened was all about one of the characters having a miscarriage. The tension in the room could have been cut with a knife. Every time a scene came on involving the miscarriage, everyone would start talking about something else. I know that they meant well, but I felt that they were avoiding my loss. I got very upset.

I got very depressed around this time and in the following weeks. I needed someone to talk to but felt that I didn't want to pick up a phone and speak to a stranger. I felt very alone and as if I was the only woman ever to go through this. I just wanted to know that what I was going through was normal.

I got no counselling from the hospital, nor was I told of anywhere that could help me. Throughout all of this my husband felt very isolated. All of the attention was focused on me. He felt somehow that, from the way he was excluded from things, he had nothing to do with it. He suffered as well. What people didn't understand was that he too had lost his baby.

Time has eased the pain. Until recently, we couldn't

think about having another baby. Now we are planning to try for a baby in August. It will never replace the baby we lost and we wouldn't want it to. What we do hope is that it will fill the terrible void in our lives, left by losing our first baby.

At times I look back at the miscarriage and wish that I had been a little further on in the pregnancy. Then I would have seen my baby and have the memory of what he or she would have looked like. I would have been able to say goodbye.

That overwhelming grief has subsided and we now look forward to the future, a future that will include children. We hope that the coming year will bring us hope, happiness and most importantly of all, a healthy baby.'

## Molly's story

*Molly was born in Co. Cavan in 1935. As a traveller, she has lived all over Ireland and also in England. She has ten children living, two boys and eight girls. She and her husband live in a Dublin suburb. In 1958 Molly gave birth to a stillborn boy.*

'At that time, travelling women never even went inside the door of a doctor's and there were no antenatal clinics. There was another travelling woman who was expecting around the same time and she saw me getting bigger then going smaller and I wasn't looking the best, so she told me to go to a doctor. No matter how sick you were or how badly you felt, the travelling women always had to do the begging because there was no dole. I was begging in the town and I went to the doctor. He examined me and said that my baby was dead.

The next day I was in Mullingar and called for an ambulance. I had no address so I had to wait outside a cottage for the ambulance; it was hours and hours before the ambulance came. It was three days before I went into labour and in those days they didn't have much for the pain. When I went into labour I hadn't a clue what it would be like with a stillborn, I thought perhaps that it might be a little easier. I was nearly three days in the labour ward in bad pain. The doctor I had seen in the town said that he was to be told when I went into labour because he would attend the birth. But there was a nurse there who thought that she would just do her own routine because this birth would be "easy done". I was in a very, very bad way and when the doctor did come, he just knocked me out with an injection. It was all over when I came to. I was told when I asked that it was a boy. I didn't see him and after I left hospital I went to England.'

*Two years later Molly had a healthy baby girl. Two years after that, in 1962, she gave birth to another stillborn baby boy.*

'The difference with this one was that I was very small. I did go to the clinic but not regularly. I did go a long time overdue and I just knew that it was dead. What I really had was a silent toxemia and a blood pressure that didn't show up. A doctor in Mullingar told me; instead of going the full time, I should have been induced at about eight months. When it came to that time, I used to feel that I could feel the baby just lying down and dying. I have explained this to settled women because there's a lot of settled women that don't even know about this.

I went to the clinic and told them that I thought the

baby was dead because I didn't feel any movements. When they examined me, they found that the baby was dead and they decided to let me home to see if I would go into labour. Nearly eight weeks passed and I went to see the doctor. I told him that I was frightened. I asked him about whether or not the baby would be decomposing inside me because it had been dead for so long. He explained to me that the heat of my body would prevent this from happening. The doctor took me in and put me on a drip. It was only a small baby, 2½ lbs. I didn't go through what I had gone through with the first one. I didn't get to see my baby.'

*In 1971 Molly gave birth to another stillborn baby boy.*

'I was allowed to see this baby. He was a big baby – 8lbs 2oz. He was the biggest of all my stillborn babies and to me he looked huge. He was a beautiful baby and I felt very sad because he was the only baby I had seen. He looked just like he was asleep and I was very glad to have seen him. When I did see him, I thought back to the time I had my first stillborn baby and how much things had changed since then.'

## Julie's story

*Julie is nineteen years old. She gave birth to a stillborn baby girl at twenty-four weeks. She is unemployed and left school when she was fourteen years old. She has gone to England in the hope of finding work and making a fresh start. I spoke to her six months after the birth.*

'I was always a bit of a rebel and couldn't wait to leave home. There was eight of us at home and we were always fighting. My Ma and Da hadn't got much time for us and spent most nights down the pub. I left school as soon as I could and worked at cleaning for a while. This didn't last long and soon I just hung around the corner most days with me mates. None of us had much money, so we used to spend our time talking about getting married and having kids. I knocked around with a couple of fellas over the years, nothing heavy now, I didn't sleep with them, it was all just a bit of fun. Then I met Jim. He was four years older than me and I thought that he was the best thing since sliced bread. I couldn't believe my luck when he started to show an interest in me, soon we were going out together.

He had a bedsit and it wasn't long before I moved in with him. Everything was fine until I became pregnant. I knew that me getting pregnant wasn't part of our plans but I really thought that it wouldn't make a difference to us. I didn't get pregnant on purpose, if anything it was his fault. One night he came in from the pub and wanted to have sex. We had no condoms and he said 'Sure, you're not going to get pregnant from just once.'

I didn't think much about it again, until about two months later when I realised that I hadn't gotten a period in a while. It didn't cross my mind that I could be pregnant and I just decided to wait until the following month. Six weeks later I still hadn't had a period and I was really worried. It was then that I realised that I could be pregnant. I tried to work out how long it had been since I last had a period and realised that I must be at least three months gone. I was worried sick and didn't know what to do, so I went to the doctor. He confirmed that I was pregnant and estimated that I was about fourteen weeks on.

I burst into tears on the way back to the bedsit and ended up sitting in a park for four hours. I was only seventeen, had no regular job and lived in a pokey bedsit that there wasn't even room to swing a cat in. On top of all of that I knew that breaking the news to Jim wouldn't be easy. I knew that he'd be there when I got in and I didn't know what to say to him.

As I turned the key in the door, my stomach was in a knot. He was sitting watching the telly and when he saw me he asked me, where the hell was I. Then he noticed the state I was in and asked me what was wrong with me. At this point I just broke down and all I wanted was for him to put his arms around me and tell me everything would be all right. He did put his arms around me and I thought that telling him mightn't be so hard after all. I tried to stop crying and took a deep breath. 'I'm pregnant, Jim, about three months.'

The next thing I remember is being thrown across the room and him screaming at me that I needn't think that I was going to trap him like this. He screamed at me that he didn't want a brat and that I'd better do something about it. That was the final straw for me, I told him that the only thing I was going to do about it was to have the baby. When I said that he turned into a lunatic and began pulling all my clothes out of the wardrobe and throwing them on the bed. He went around the place grabbing anything he could find belonging to me and started throwing them into a black sack. I was screaming at him to stop but he wouldn't.

All of a sudden he stopped tearing around the place and came over to where I was. He looked into my face and told me that if I wasn't gone by the time he got back, I would need hospital treatment and that I wouldn't have to worry about being pregnant anymore. He grabbed my keys which were still in my hand and said that I had two hours to be gone. He said that anything that was left belonging to me would be burnt.

As the door slammed behind him, I sank to the ground. I had never been as scared in me life. I thought about slitting my wrists but then thought about the baby. It was my baby and I knew that for its safety and my own I had to get out, and fast. I packed what I could into plastic sacks and got a taxi to me Ma's. When I got there, it was obvious that I was not welcome so I decided not to tell them that I was pregnant. They told me that I could stay there until I found somewhere else to go. A couple of weeks later I was eighteen and could get the dole. The week I got the dole, I bought the evening papers and looked for a flat. I managed to find one on the other side of the city and moved in that same night. The last thing me Ma said to me was 'Don't come back here if it doesn't work out.' As I sat in my flat that night, I have never felt as lonely or afraid as I was then.

I attended the hospital for my visits and everything was going well. The social worker in the hospital had a chat with me and told me what I would be entitled to when the baby was born. She was the only person I ever spoke to.

When the baby started kicking, I felt that I was not alone any more. I couldn't afford to buy any baby clothes, so I used to buy a ball of wool every week and knit little cardigans. I talked to the baby all the time and promised it that, no matter what, I would be the best mother ever. I got to know the baby's resting times and also when it was most active. When my tummy began getting bigger I felt that at last I had done something with my life. I got a little box and put anything I got for the baby in it. I used to go around the charity shops looking for nearly new vests and stuff. I didn't know much about what having a baby

51

was like and I worried about the pain, so when I went for a visit at twenty-two weeks I asked the doctor how bad would the pain be, and he told me that I could get an injection that would take the pain away. This cheered me up. I had a chart hanging on the wall in the flat counting the days until the baby was due, and every night I'd mark off that day.

When I was about twenty-four weeks pregnant, I noticed that the baby wasn't kicking that much. I didn't worry because I thought that it was probably just tired. The next night I still hadn't felt it move and began to think that maybe it shouldn't be asleep for that long. I tried to see if I could wake it up by poking my tummy but this didn't work. I didn't know what to do and thought that it was too late to ring the hospital, I decided to phone first thing in the morning.

I woke up the next morning with my hands still on my stomach. I got dressed and went out to the call box to ring the hospital. I explained to the nurse what was wrong expecting her to tell me that I was worrying too much, so I was surprised when she told me to come in immediately.

She told me that they would do a scan and I remember that I was happy that I'd see the baby on the telly again. At this stage I wasn't worried that something was very wrong and didn't even think about bringing a nightdress. I was a bit sad that I had nobody to talk to and I remember wishing that I wasn't so alone.

When I got to the hospital, I asked for the nurse I was talking to and she took me to the scan straight away. A doctor came over to me and asked me some questions, I began to get a bit worried then. I asked him what did he think was wrong and he said that the scan would be able to tell him that. He put the jelly on my tummy and began moving the yoke across, I was looking at the telly to see if I could see the baby and I did. I was excited and asked the doctor if he could tell if it was a girl or a boy. He didn't answer me and called the nurse over. I looked over at the nurse to tell her to look at the baby on the screen and she wasn't smiling like I thought she would be. I was a bit puzzled at this and turned to look at the doctor, he wouldn't look at me. Then I got the feeling that something was wrong and I wanted to know what it was.

Before I had a chance to ask, the doctor wiped the jelly off my tummy and sat on the bed beside me. He put his arm around me and said to me that he had some very bad news. Even then, I didn't know what the bad news could be. He turned to me, looked me straight in the eye and said, 'I'm so sorry, your baby has died.' The first thing I did was laugh, I thought that it was all a sick joke. Then I thought that he had made a mistake. Then it hit me. My baby, my only friend in the world, had died and left me all alone. I couldn't really think straight and asked the doctor to show me my baby on the telly again. When he did, I looked at the baby and said to the doctor that he didn't look dead. I remember thinking that he couldn't be dead, I wanted him so much.

Then I lost control completely. I began screaming at the doctor and even went to hit him. It was then that the nurse took me in her arms and told me to let it all out. It was the first time since I got pregnant that somebody cared enough to hold me. I was so frightened and so upset. Now, at the worst time in my life, when I needed somebody, I was on my own and had no-one I could turn to for help. I sat on that bed and cried for a very long time. Then I started to think about what would happen next. I knew that the baby couldn't stay inside me and I wondered how it would come out.

The doctor then explained that he felt it would be best if I was admitted right away and induced. It hit me then, I'd still have to go through with the birth but I'd have no baby to take home at the end of it. I was frightened because I didn't know what was going to happen to me and I was afraid to be on my own. The nurse was the best friend I ever had. She promised to stay with me until it was all over. I was in a daze and kept thinking that all this was just a dream. I couldn't believe that it was happening and I just wanted someone to tell me that they had made a mistake. I was hooked up to a drip and six hours later I began to get pains.

The pain got worse and I thought that I was dying; it seemed to go on forever and then I got an injection. It was like magic, the pain wasn't so bad anymore and I was able to lie still. I kept asking what the birth would be like and what the baby would be like. I kept saying that it was my baby and I wanted to see it. I didn't want them to think that I was just a kid, so I kept saying, if I am old enough to have this baby, I'm old enough to see it. They reassured me that I could see my baby.

When the nurse went to get a cup of tea, I just lay there thinking. I was angry at God for letting this happen. This baby was all I had in the world and the only person that would have loved me truly. This baby was my future, why had it died. I wondered was it something I had done, I wondered was it because I couldn't afford to eat good food all the time, I wondered was it because the baby didn't want me as a mother. Then the nurse came back and took a look at me, she told me that it was almost time for my baby to be born.

As I was wheeled into the labour ward, I could hear babies cry and I said to the nurse, 'Why couldn't it have been one of them?' The doctor gave me another injection so I was in no pain. I couldn't really feel anything and then I felt a sensation, it was as if I had gone to the toilet. They had a sheet covering me from the waist down, so I couldn't see anything. I saw my nurse cry and the doctor turned to me and said that it was a beautiful baby girl. I asked if I could see her, and they said that as soon as they had weighed her and cleaned her up, I could.

The nurse then tried to tell me what she would look like. She told me that she would not look like the kind of new baby that I was used to seeing and that she was very, very small. I was a little bit afraid of seeing her, I had never seen a dead baby before and I didn't know what to expect.

When they did bring her to me, I just took her and held her close. I looked at her and thought that she looked just like me. She was very small, and although she wasn't like a new baby, I was not afraid of her. I spent a long time with her and felt so sad because she had a daddy and grandparents that would never even see her. On seeing her face, the name I had picked for a girl, suited her. I called her Hope. All those months ago I said to myself, 'If this baby is a girl I'll call her Hope because that is what she has given me.' As I looked at my baby, it was as if she was only asleep.

I went to see her again before I left the hospital. All I had with me were the clothes I had come in. I did have a thin gold bracelet on and before I said goodbye to her, I took my bracelet off and put it around her neck. I then asked for a photograph to be taken. It is all I have of Hope and I carry it everywhere. I did not attend her burial because I felt that it was something that I just couldn't do on my own. I did go and visit the grave the following week. I brought with me the two cardigans that I had knitted and buried them under the clay on her grave. I will never forget her.

After I came home from hospital I knew that now there was nothing here for me any more. I collected my dole and bought a one way ticket to England. I don't know what I'll find there, I don't even know what I'll do there; but one thing is certain, nothing can be as bad as the last year. I still pray that one day I will meet a nice man and settle down and have another baby. A brother or sister for Hope would be nice.'

## Lorraine's story

*My best friend, Lorraine, is thirty years old, single and has a six-year-old daughter. Nine years ago her son was stillborn at twenty-six weeks.*

'It was a big shock when I first found out that I was pregnant. I was only twenty-one and getting pregnant was the last thing on my mind. I didn't tell my mother or father that I was pregnant but I told the rest of my family. They were great and all rallied around me, giving me the support that I needed. My boyfriend stood by me and, after the initial shock of my pregnancy wore off, we began to look forward to the arrival of our baby.

I went to the hospital for my first visit and I was told that the baby was due on the 2nd of October. Everything was fine and, apart from morning sickness that lasted all day and night, the pregnancy progressed normally until the sixteenth week.

One morning when I was sixteen weeks pregnant, I noticed that I was bleeding. I went straight to the hospital and was admitted for bedrest. After two days the bleeding stopped and, after being examined by the doctor, it was decided that everything was fine and I was out of danger. I was allowed to go home. At this stage I told my mother that I was pregnant and that I had nearly lost the baby; she was shocked but stood by me. From then on, I had a mother's love and support to rely on.

Some weeks later I returned to the hospital for another visit, everything was fine and I felt so happy. I bought some baby clothes in pink and blue and began buying something for the baby every week. As my bump began to show, my morning sickness stopped, and when I felt the baby kick for the first time it really hit me that there was actually a baby inside me. I was really looking forward to the birth now.

I was twenty-six weeks pregnant when one morning I got out of bed and suddenly there was a huge gush of water running down my legs. I didn't know what was happening and totally panicked. I screamed for my friend who was staying with me at the time, she told me that I should go to the hospital. Before I did anything I rang my sister and told her what had happened, she also told me to go straight to the hospital and she would meet me there. I got to the hospital and was examined; the doctor wasn't sure whether or not my waters had broken. I was admitted for observation and bedrest. The baby was monitored and everything was normal, the heartbeat was perfect. I presumed that this time was going to be just like the last and I would be allowed to go home in a couple of days. The only thing that worried me was the fact that I was still losing water.

For the next two days there was no change. I was more worried than the first time I was taken in, but tried to push it to the back of my mind. When my boyfriend and family came to visit, I thought that they would never leave so I could stop the charade and stop pretending that I was fine.

On the Friday night, two days after I was admitted, the baby's heartbeat was monitored and everything was fine. The next morning I started getting cramps. I thought that I was constipated so I went to the toilet. As I was sitting on the toilet, something started to come down and I began screaming. A nurse came in and tried to reassure me, telling me that everything would be all right. She then brought me back to the ward. All of a sudden it was as if all hell had broken loose; there were doctors and nurses everywhere.

A doctor examined me and told me that the cord had come down. He put it back up and then told me, quite matter of factly, that in the next few hours I was going to lose my baby. He said that even if they performed a section, there was no guarantee that the baby would live. He said that the best thing to do would be to let the labour progress spontaneously. I pleaded with him to give me a section because my baby was alive, but he refused, saying, 'You have to think of yourself recovering from a section and maybe for nothing.' I was then asked if there was anyone I would like to contact. I rang my sister who came in immediately accompanied by my brother-in-law and my friend that was with me when this all started.

Even then I kept praying that everything would be all right. I knew that the baby would be premature, but he was alive and right now that was all that mattered. At 11 a.m. I was taken to be prepared for the impending birth. My boyfriend arrived and together we waited. A couple of hours later, a nurse came to monitor the baby and couldn't find a heartbeat. I remember saying to her, 'My baby's dead isn't it?' and she said 'Yes'. I couldn't believe what she had said to me – this all felt as if it was happening to someone else. I went numb and started to cry. My boyfriend went out to tell my sister, brother-in-law and friend who were waiting outside. They were all as shocked as we were and couldn't believe that this had happened either. Everyone was crying and I was in shock, I think we all were. Almost immediately after it was discovered that my baby had died, I began getting very bad contractions. These went on for the next seven hours and at 8 p.m. I was taken into the labour ward. I was in the labour ward for four hours and I was given gas and pethidine for the pain.

I still expected at the end of all of this to have a baby; it had happened too quickly for it to be real and actually happening to me. At 11.45 p.m. the pain intensified, and at 12.03 a.m. I felt a strange sensation, like a plop. This was in fact my son being born. Everyone was crying and the nurse took him away to clean him up before handing him to me. When I saw him, he just looked as if he was fast asleep. He was very, very small but perfect in every way. He was the image of his daddy and I couldn't believe that this was my son.

My boyfriend and I were left alone with him and a nurse came in and asked us what we were going to name him. At this stage neither of us could think straight, we hadn't discussed names yet and now we were being asked for one. Neither of us could function properly and the nurse said to us that it was the feast day of St John the Baptist, so we called our son Baby John. We said our goodbyes and then a nurse brought Baby John out to my sister, brother-in-law and friend to give them a chance to say their own goodbyes. I later learnt that they all said prayers with Baby John.

It was about 3 a.m. when everyone left and I was taken to a ward. I felt so empty and numb, I couldn't take in all that had happened in the space of a few hours. I had gone from being happily pregnant to nothing. I didn't sleep that night, and when family came to visit later that day, I remember feeling sorry for them because nobody knew what to say to me. They all said how sorry they were, of course, but it was a situation that nobody ever expected to be in. The rest of that day passed in a blur and the following morning a nurse asked me if I would like to see Baby John before they performed the autopsy. My boyfriend came in and we both went to see Baby John, who was in the morgue.

To get to the morgue, it was necessary to pass through the ante-natal clinic, and as I walked through it, looking at all the women with their bumps, I prayed that nobody would ever have to go through what I was going through. I was very upset seeing all these pregnant women.

When I got to the morgue, I remember feeling everything was so cold. My baby was just lying on a slab, clothed only in a gown. He had a flower in his hands and he looked so peaceful. As I looked at him, I knew that this would be the last time I would ever see my baby; my heart was breaking. After we said our last goodbye to Baby John, we went back to the ward, where my mother and father were waiting. I remember crying and saying to them, 'He only looks as if he's asleep.' The next morning I was discharged. It was very upsetting to leave the hospital emptyhanded after so many dreams. I went to my sister's house and stayed there until the funeral two days later. Those two days passed in a blur and the morning of the funeral arrived.

My sister brought us to the cemetery. I wanted it private, just myself and my boyfriend. The family couldn't understand this, but accepted that it was how I felt. I have regretted this decision many times since; I feel that I should have given Baby John's relatives the chance to say goodbye to him. My boyfriend carried the coffin from the hearse and I couldn't quite take in that my baby was inside that tiny white coffin. He placed the coffin on top of the two planks that covered the grave and, as there was no priest, we said our own prayers and silent goodbyes to Baby John. We left the cemetery and came home. On the way home I remember wanting to scream at people because I had just buried my son and they didn't care.

In the following weeks there were many times when I just wanted to kill myself. I felt that I had nothing left to live for and didn't eat or sleep; my life was meaningless. As Baby John's 'birth date' approached, I found it very hard to cope with. To make matters worse, my friend who had been with me through all of this, gave birth to a healthy baby boy three weeks after Baby John should have been born. This broke my heart.

It took a long time to start functioning normally again and to accept that nothing I could have done would have prevented what happened. The autopsy showed that physically Baby John was perfect and the cause of death was the cord. In a way this made me feel a little better, but in another way I felt that perhaps the doctor involved had played God with my baby.

Three years later I became pregnant again, and in June 1987, three years and three days after Baby John's birth, I gave birth in the same cubicle as Baby John, to a healthy baby girl. She is six now and has helped to heal a lot of the pain. To this day however, even though nine years have passed, Baby John's birth and face is still as vivid as if it were only yesterday.'

## Ann's story

*Ann is in her late twenties, married and living in Co. Dublin. She has had three consecutive miscarriages in a fourteen-month period. At the time we met it was three months since her last miscarriage. She has no other children.*

'When we got married we planned to have children straight away. We both loved children and wanted to start our family as soon as possible, so we were over the moon when it was confirmed that I was pregnant. It was like a dream come true and we rushed to tell our families our good news. We wanted everyone to share our happiness.

When I was almost eight weeks pregnant, I had a miscarriage. I was physically in a lot of pain and couldn't believe that this was happening. The miscarriage was complete so I didn't need a D&C or to stay in hospital overnight. I was absolutely devastated and consumed with the desire to become pregnant again straight away. I was anxious all the time, and when after five months I still wasn't pregnant, I went to see the doctor. He told me that it was quite normal to take this long to conceive and that it could take a lot longer. He told me that I needed to relax a little and try and direct my thoughts to something that wasn't to do with becoming pregnant. After this visit I felt more relaxed, and a couple of weeks later became pregnant.

With the second pregnancy, I was sick from day one. I was so bad with this sickness I had to give up work. I felt wretched all the time and wondered when the sickness would end. When I had got past the stage at which I lost the other baby, I began to look at baby books and dream about the baby I was carrying.

After a routine visit to the hospital at thirteen and a half weeks, a scan revealed that my baby had died. I had a D&C and went home the following morning. The doctor told me that my miscarriage was in fact a missed abortion – when a foetus dies in the uterus and is not expelled.

When I got home I felt a terrible sense of loneliness. I began asking myself was I a freak? What was wrong with me? I felt a terrible sense of loss and knew that the only thing that would help me was to become pregnant again. After what seemed like an eternity, four months later I became pregnant.

This time we told nobody. I didn't want to go through it all again if anything went wrong. I was very nervous and was afraid even to think about a successful pregnancy. Unlike the other two, I wasn't sick from the beginning. I remember thinking to myself that this could be a good sign. However, at seven weeks the sickness started, and got so bad soon everybody in work knew that I was pregnant, and a couple of weeks later I was so sick all the time I had to give up work. Even at home, the slightest thing would make me nauseous; it got to the stage that the smell of the fibre of the new carpet was making me ill. To try and lessen this, I went to stay with my parents for a few days a week.

I waited until I was nearly nine weeks pregnant before I went to the hospital. When I did go, I was scanned and the doctor said that everything was perfect. I remember saying to the doctor, 'I have already lost two and I don't want anything to happen to this one.' He told me not to worry, everything was fine. I was very, very happy and began to think about the baby. I didn't care about the sickness, I just kept telling myself that it wouldn't last forever. I knew that

I could contend with anything if, at the end of the day, I held my baby in my arms. Although afraid, I began hoping.

Before my visit at twelve and a half weeks, I began to feel strange. I couldn't pinpoint what made me feel like this, but I felt that something was wrong. In retrospect what happened was that I began to stop 'feeling' pregnant, but I didn't realise this at the time.

As I sat in the queue with my husband for my ante-natal visit at twelve weeks, I turned to him and said, 'The baby's dead'. He told me that I was only being over-anxious and not to worry. When I was finally called to see the doctor, I walked into the room full of fear and desolation. Before I was even examined I had a feeling that I would be told that the baby had died. My fears were realised when the doctor couldn't find a heartbeat for the baby. He said that he would try to locate a heartbeat on a different machine upstairs and asked me to go for a cup of coffee and fill my bladder as much as I could.

As I sat drinking coffee with my husband, I knew that it was all in vain, I knew that my baby had died and that no machine in the hospital would be able to find a heartbeat. We returned to the hospital and I was brought to a different machine. Again they tried to find the heartbeat but couldn't. Eventually, the doctor turned to me and said, 'I'm so sorry, your baby has died.' I immediately ran out to my husband who was waiting outside and told him. I had a D&C a couple of hours later and went home the following morning. I was devastated.

The feeling of hopelessness overwhelmed me and I felt a complete failure. I spent all my time wondering what was wrong with me and why I couldn't have a baby. The fact that this was my third miscarriage in such a short period of time also meant that it was very difficult for people to talk to me. I felt that people were avoiding me because they were embarrassed about what to say to me. A couple of neighbours were expecting babies and I was worried about how I would react to seeing them now that I had had a third miscarriage. When I did see them, I felt fairly okay and was actually more concerned about their discomfort seeing me. I am lucky that my neighbours are also good friends and that they understand how I feel. They have been very good and have brought me flowers and cards to show that they care about what has happened and realise how I feel. What hasn't helped me is all the people who tell me I can try again. They say it as if it's the easiest thing in the world to do, to just forget about the babies I have lost, to pretend that what happened wasn't important and to just 'get on with it'.

The most upsetting thing that happened was actually at a family gathering a short time after my last miscarriage. We were all seated around the table having dinner when my husband's brother, who has four children, turned to my husband and said to him 'What's wrong with her?', referring to the fact that I had had three miscarriages. This was terribly upsetting not only for me but also for my husband. It seemed quite sad that the most distressing comment had come from a member of our family. None of my husband's family understand what we have been through. Because they have all had children with no problems, they can't understand why I can't just get pregnant and have a baby like anyone else. Not one of them asked me how I was, nor did they ask if I needed anything. I felt like an outcast and just wish that they would understand the pain and suffering that my miscarriages have caused.

As the 'due' date falls for each of the babies I lost, I

think about them and how it might have been. In two months' time I am going into hospital for tests to determine whether or not there is something physically wrong with me. If nothing shows up, we plan to try for another baby immediately. If something does show up, we hope that it can be treated and that I will be able to have a successful pregnancy. No matter what, I will keep trying because I will never feel complete until I am holding a baby at the end of a successful pregnancy.

Having had so many miscarriages, people seem to be of the opinion that it almost becomes a habit to have a miscarriage, but this is not true. The only thing that becomes habit is the hospital routine following the miscarriage – you begin to know what to expect. But the pain and grief of losing baby after baby is something that I could *never* just get used to. Each miscarriage is painful and the sense of loss and emptiness doesn't subside because you have had more than one, if anything it gets a little worse each time and the feeling of failure becomes greater.

Despite all that we have gone through, my husband and I will continue to try for a much wanted baby. We know that at the end of the day, all the pain and suffering will not have been in vain and we pray that some day our dream to have a baby will come true. Through this, we have realised how precious life is and how easy it is to take things for granted.'

# Fathers grieve too

After a miscarriage or stillbirth many fathers feel isolated and left out of things, their needs and grief unnoticed. They often find it hard to talk about their feelings or to show any emotion in public. It can seem that no-one really understands his pain and, at times, that no-one really cares.

In the hospital, the father feels helpless and frustrated because all he can do is watch whilst the doctors look after his partner. Because she is so distressed, he has to try and be strong for her, sometimes hiding his own grief. His partner turns to him for comfort and support during this traumatic time and he is expected to be there for her without any thought for his own emotions.

On top of the heartbreak of losing his baby, the father has to cope with many practical matters. If there are other children, he has to go home from the hospital and explain to them what has happened. He has to contact other family members. If the pregnancy has reached the stage where a funeral is necessary, it is usually he who has to make the arrangements. He has to contend with all of this whilst trying to come to terms with what has happened, sometimes not getting an opportunity to discuss his own feelings.

**Early miscarriage**
With an early miscarriage, there is no tangible evidence of the baby so the father has nothing to

remember his child by. He grieves for the baby he never got the chance to see but in most cases his main concern is for his partner.

Sometimes after an early miscarriage a communication problem can arise between the parents. It is quite common for a woman to be ultra-sensitive and to be very weepy. She is often mixed up both emotionally and physically and is emotionally charged. The husband may fall victim to her feelings of anger and guilt. She may accuse him of not caring because he is not going around crying all the time, or tell him that he doesn't care about the miscarriage or can't know what it feels like.

These are common, normal reactions of grief. In this situation it is better just to let the mother get it out of her system without shouting back. The parents may blame each other for the miscarriage, but this kind of exchange solves nothing. The miscarriage is nobody's fault and nothing would have prevented it from happening. Ordinary actions and events can be easily misconstrued: the only way to avoid this happening is for couples to talk to each other about how they feel and to be honest and open with each other. They should try to find relatives or friends to confide in. The important thing is to find an outlet for the feelings of grief, anger, or despair and be able to release them.

**Late miscarriage/stillbirth**
When a baby is stillborn, the father is more involved than with an early miscarriage. There is tangible evidence that a baby has died and the grief and recognition are more intense. A father can only speculate about a baby lost early in pregnancy, but with a stillbirth he is faced with the reality of what has happened when he sees his baby's face.

Many men are shocked by the intense feelings they experience from the time they know that their baby has died, or will die. When Glen was born, my husband was totally unprepared for the surge of emotion he felt. Although he had known for four weeks that our baby would die, and two weeks before he was born that he had died, nothing could have prepared him for the moment he first saw his son's face. He said that there was no comparison between my early miscarriages and the stillbirth. With the stillbirth he was able to see and hold his baby, with the miscarriages he was not.

Fathers may feel that it is their responsibility to remain calm and composed during the time at the hospital following the birth. This should not be so and a man should cry if he feels like crying and not feel embarrassed because other people might think that it is 'unmanly' to do so. In a situation like this, there is no such thing as an accepted way to behave. Every person is different, and the birth of a stillborn baby is devastating for every parent.

The time spent at the hospital with the baby is very, very short and it is important that the father spends that time saying and doing what he wants to and not worrying about what people might think. When a man finds himself holding back tears or not asking if he can hold his baby one last time in case people think that he's being weak, he should remember that no doctor or nurse in the hospital would retain their composure if they came face to face with their own stillborn baby. It is possible to remain calm when the stillborn baby you are holding is not your own; fathers should remember this if they feel embarrassed about crying or despairing.

They should ask for help and accept any that is offered. There is no need to try and cope with everything without any help when there are so many people ready to assist in any way they can. This is not the first stillbirth to take place in the hospital, and because of this staff are familiar with procedure and the emotion that follows a stillbirth.

## Fathers' grief should be recognised

After a miscarriage or stillbirth so much attention is focused on the mother people tend to forget that two parents have lost their child. It is very upsetting for a man to be asked how his partner is, without any reference to his own wellbeing, when he too has buried his child.

Failure to ask the father how he is may cause him to grieve for his own personal grief. He will grieve because he has not been recognised as a father and the baby is not recognised as his baby. He will grieve for his lost identity.

One thing to remember is that people are not being malicious when they ask only about the mother; if they have never been in this situation they don't realise that it is not just the mother who has suffered a loss. On the whole people mean well, and their interest in the mother's as opposed to the parents' well-being is not unkindly meant.

The onus for accepting the father's grief lies not with him, but with all those who come into contact with him. He is more than aware of his own grief. He needs the understanding of others to help him come to terms with it.

# Glen's Song

## by Gerry Colgan

I can't believe what we heard tonight,
Our unborn child may never see the light,
With six months gone and only three to go,
There's something wrong the doctors can't control.
My wife went in with just bad back pain,
Now there's so much more, they say we're not to
    blame,
At 30 weeks they'll do what they can do,
But the baby's getting sicker and the odds are getting
    few.

I can't believe what the doctors say,
'Sorry there's no cure, just hope and pray,
Take your wife home, come back for weekly tests,
It's hard we know, try and see she rests.'
This Christmas time's so hard to bear,
With our two year old son we try and share,
We feel so helpless, we hold on tight,
Please God our baby's strong enough to fight.

I can't believe what we heard today,
The news is bad; your baby's passed away,
There is no heartbeat or movement in the womb,
We'll try some pills to bring on labour soon.
Two weeks have passed and it's so unreal,
Our hearts are breaking, such pain we feel.
The pills have failed and Mother Nature's slow,
My wife can't bear to let our baby go.

I can't believe what I saw today,
My wife  gave birth, they took our son away.
After so much pain, she was denied her wish,
He never got the chance to cry or kick,
We held him close and I tried to sing,
How much we love and needed him.
Pass an exit sign through an entrance door,
Our baby's coming home no more.

He had his mother's eyes and his father's mouth,
But he'll never see, taste or shout.
His grandmother's nose without a doubt,
Hands small and perfect but they'll never reach out.

I can't explain how I felt today,
As we laid our child beneath the clay.
A time to part, a farewell touch,
Our little Glen to God we trust.

In Heaven now our angel sings,
We live each day and think of him,
Through photographs and nightmare dreams,
Of all that was and could have been.

*December 1989 – January 1990*

# Gerry's story

When Karina decided to write this book, I was puzzled. Why? Why couldn't she just let it be? Why go through it all again, the pain, the anger, the despair and that horrible feeling of helplessness. Why drag up the past again? But in time I realised why she was undertaking such a commitment. In some ways the past is ever present and, though now the pain has dulled, some memories remain frightfully vivid.

For me as husband and father during this most difficult time in our lives, I found it very hard at times to come to terms with my own feelings. As a boy I used to watch John Wayne as he demonstrated the role of the 'real' man: strong, silent and never failing to protect and serve. I found myself torn between expressing my true feelings of helplessness and despair or showing the side of me that I had been conditioned to express. What role was I to play? Could I be me, could I allow myself to fall apart, especially in a predominantly female environment? I felt isolated and alone. This was, after all, my baby too.

The nightmare began with a phone call from Karina. She was very upset and I could barely make out what she was saying. After she calmed down a little, she explained that a scan had showed that there was something wrong. The doctor had suggested that she ring me and ask me to get to the hospital as soon as possible and when I arrived she would explain everything. I searched for words of comfort and told her not to worry, whilst my mind raced for answers. I promised that I'd be there as soon as possible, but it still hadn't hit me. It was only when I explained to my friend Ger that something was wrong with Karina's pregnancy that I began to realise the importance of what I had just said.

Waiting for a bus into town, I tried to reason things out whilst I chain-smoked and paced the footpath. What could be wrong? After what seemed like a lifetime, I finally got a bus. The confinement of being in such a tiny place aggravated me and I began to panic. I felt my head spin and I thought that I was going to get sick. It reminded me of a time when, as a boy, I had got the wrong bus and ended up in a place miles from home. I was frightened and crying when the bus conductor came over to me and told me not to worry, that he'd see that I got home. As this memory faded I wondered, if I cried now, would somebody come over to me and tell me that everything would be all right?

When I got off the bus, I went to walk across O'Connell Bridge, but I needed another cigarette so I leaned against the cold grey columns of the bridge whilst I smoked another cigarette. Then, instead of going to the hospital, I turned and went to a music shop. At the time it didn't make much sense; Karina was waiting for me to arrive. She was very upset and needed comfort and here was I strolling around a music shop. Why? Looking back now, I think that it was because I was so scared and music had always been a great escape.

After maybe five minutes I knew that I had to go to the hospital. When I got to the ward the screen was pulled; I didn't know if Karina was alone so I called her name. She stood up and pulled the curtains. She looked exhausted, her face was tear-stained and her eyes were red and sore. I took her in my arms and told her everything would be okay, I didn't know what else I could say. Soon after, my mother-in-law arrived. When the doctor came she took us to the scan room. I just wanted to know what the problem was right away. The doctor delicately informed us that our baby was in a lot of distress and that the chances of it surviving were very slim. Now truly the nightmare had begun. Karina's sobs punctuated the doctor's words of sympathy. I felt a cold sweat breaking out and a shiver ran down my spine. I thought to myself 'So this is what "There's something wrong" means.'

We slowly walked back to the ward and tried to rationalise the news. We said that doctors can be wrong and that maybe we were given the worst scenario just in case it happened. After my mother-in-law went home, we walked the corridors together hardly knowing what to say or do. As we said goodbye we hugged one another and again I told her not to worry. I remember her pulling back and looking into my eyes. Did I really believe that, or was I just as scared as she was? I left her with the infamous words 'Don't worry', knowing that that was exactly what she would do until we saw each other again.

The next few weeks proved to be extremely stressful, and what I couldn't talk about I wrote down as lyrics, poems or whatever form they took. I was very scared of the future but I needed to remain strong. Karina attended the hospital but, though there was no good news, we still hoped. Karina didn't leave the house much; it was too difficult for her to face people and their well-meaning questions. These people knew nothing of our hidden grief. I was finding it hard to answer questions like 'How's your wife?' or 'It won't be long now until there's another one running around.' What was I to say? 'Well, actually our baby is going to die'?

Friends and family were supportive and helped us in any way they could. We both knew though, that sooner or later it had to come to an end. There were times that I wished for a quick birth regardless of the outcome, but these were few compared to those when I wanted things to remain the way they were, while we still had hope.

Christmas was soon upon us, but we didn't care, it meant nothing. We tried to be cheerful for Karl but failed. After Christmas, time seemed to pass very slowly and the end of each day was now the beginning of a restless night. We had talked so much about everything, there came a stage when we had nothing more to say. I remember Karina getting very upset because I was reading a magazine: she shouted that it seemed that the magazine was more important than our baby.

On New Year's Eve, after having no movement from the baby all day, Karina was very worried and so was I. My John Wayne charade was wearing very thin; soon I would have to face my deepest fears. How would I handle things? When we arrived at the hospital later that evening, I was petrified and wondered if this was the end. We were taken to the scan room and a nurse put a sensor around Karina's stomach. I stood beside the bed holding her hand and telling her it would be all right.

I watched closely as the nurse performed the now familiar routine and, as I moved quietly adjusting my weight from one foot to the other, I thought it strange that it was taking so long. The nurse couldn't get a reading and summoned a doctor. After he tried for a while, he turned to my wife and said that he was sorry but he had some 'bad news'. He said that he was so sorry but our baby was dead.

The next few minutes are still a blur. I remember

helping Karina from the bed and being brought to a private room where we were given tea. I remember my mother-in-law rubbing my arm and looking so very sad. I leaned my head against the wall, and as I looked at Karina , I felt utterly helpless.

After a while we called for the doctor and told him that we wanted to go home. He explained the options we had and it was decided that Karina would be induced a few days later. He also suggested to me that it might be a good idea for me to have a friend with me during this time. I took the doctor's advice and telephoned my best friend, Ger, who came in straight away. The doctor was right, I needed to talk to someone of the same sex. When Ger arrived he didn't say much, but he listened which was what I needed. I felt lost for words, I was in some kind of emotional trance and kept wondering how was this happening, our baby was dead and still inside Karina. What a cruel twist of fate.

We left the hospital and went home. Karl, oblivious to the tragic news, was playful and happy. All I wanted to do was forget, to just drift away. I wanted to drink and get drunk, very drunk, but I didn't want to go to a pub. In the end I went to an off-licence with Ger and I bought a lot of drink. It was New Year's Eve but I wasn't celebrating. I drank quite a lot but I couldn't get drunk, I couldn't escape. At midnight, as U2 rang in the New Year, I wondered how could anyone be happy when our baby was dead. It was the beginning of a new year, a year I didn't want to bring in.

New Year's morning brought everything into horrifying perspective. I woke to find Karina still sitting there weeping, hugging baby clothes. I tried to remain strong to keep things together. Karina had withdrawn and barely spoke. I tried to comfort her but what could I say? I remember she looked at me coldly when I said 'Don't worry'.

Nothing mattered any more. We wandered through each day, each of us experiencing feelings we had never felt before. I tried to forget by switching off. I remember going to the shop for groceries and ended up in the video shop. A funny extract was playing from a forthcoming release and I forgot my sorrow and laughed uninhibitedly, but soon I came to. I couldn't run from this, it was my child who was dead and my child I would have to bury. Karina and I barely spoke now, instead we hugged and gently touched expressing the love that words could not convey.

On the morning of the 12th January 1990, Karina came into the room where I was playing with Karl. She didn't have to speak, I knew that the day had come for our baby to be born. Karina wouldn't let me telephone the hospital for a long time. When I did, I spoke to our doctor who told us to come straight in. After many tears we left for the hospital. I was still in control and everything was in order. I had to plead with Karina to come as she hesitated at the front door. I was emotionless, I had to be. I didn't want to lose our baby either, but it had to be born and Karina had to face the birth. We sat in the back of the car like prisoners en route to a firing squad.

Entering the front door of the hospital I glanced at Karina; she was composed and I wondered how long she would remain that way. In the lift her waters broke and so did her composure. It was the end, and although she couldn't bear to let go, she now had no choice. At the delivery she refused to push and was hysterical. My heart broke for her as I held her hand and watched helplessly like a neutral spectator. I told her that she had to let go. Within minutes it was all over, our baby was born and finally I let go. My whole body seemed to surge with grief as I saw the limp, blackish-grey body of my son emerge from Karina's body. My first thought was 'Oh God, how perfect he looks.'

I went to tell my mother-in-law the sex of our baby and asked her to go into Karina whilst I had a cigarette. I went into the fathers' waiting-room because it was the only place where smoking was permitted. There were two other men in the room and one turned to me and asked if it was a boy or girl. He told me not to be crying, it was all over now. When I turned to him and said that my son was dead, he looked at me as if to say, 'That's not something you say in the open.' I left the room and went to Karina. I was aware of what had happened but I think I was in shock, I could no longer feel.

I was brought to see my baby privately. Now he looked more red than black. He was wrapped in cotton-wool. Looking at him the tears returned. I cried for his loss of life, I cried for all the games we would never play, I cried for the brother he would never know and the mother he would never see, but most of all I cried for me. Looking at this tiny baby, I saw love and the heartbreak it can wield. I saw my son perfectly formed with ten fingers and ten toes that would never again move. I noticed how he resembled me and other family members. As I sat holding him, the doctor arrived. She spoke lovingly of my baby and didn't refer to him as dead in the past tense, but as Glen, our baby boy. She soon left, and before I did, I sang 'Only love can break your heart' to him. It seemed an appropriate song, it was one I'd sung many times before but never with such unbridled emotion. A nurse arrived to take Glen away and I presumed that I would see him again.

Karina was now ready to be moved to a ward. I described Glen to her and told her how perfect he looked. Karina first saw Glen with me and my mother-in-law. It was a very difficult moment and one I will never forget. That night we both sat with Glen as two of my sisters came to say goodbye to him. Later, when I went home, I wished that Karina was with me. I felt so alone and so afraid. The next morning as soon as the dawn broke, I went into the hospital. We both went to see Glen to say our final goodbye.

Karina was frightened of what the mortuary would be like, but had no need to be. It was beautifully decorated and Glen lay in a Moses basket surrounded by flowers. As Karina gave Glen to me to hold, my heart was breaking. It was a very sad farewell.

We went home shortly afterwards without our baby. I was drained. I had organised the funeral and couldn't believe that I had been able to think straight enough to deal with it.

When we got home, I was at a loss. We were both experiencing severe heartache, but Karina had carried Glen for all that time and now he was gone. I tried to comfort her but words were hard to find. People called to offer their condolences and it did help to know that so many people cared, but after many of those expressions I became extremely angry. Typically, people would offer their sympathy and ask how Karina was: 'It must be terrible for her' or 'Look after her'. On several occasions I wanted to scream and shake them into understanding how I felt.

I had been strong, I had carried on as best I could, but I still had feelings, I wasn't a rock. My son was dead and although I hadn't carried him, I had waited for him, prayed for him, longed for him and loved him. One stupid person had the insensitivity to tell me that 'It is all for the best, sure if he had lived he would have been a burden.'

I was still struggling to come to terms with my feelings; outwardly I suppose I looked as though I was coping well, but inside I was very confused. I grieved for my son, but I didn't know him. All I knew of him was what I saw after the birth: a tiny, limp baby with some of my features. Some people said to me 'Sure, you didn't even know him, it's not so bad that way.' All I can say in response to those assumptions is that I grieved for someone I had loved, and more so, for my beautiful son whom I never got the chance to know.

I became obsessed with my feelings of grief; I analysed every thought, however unimportant. Then the guilt came. 'It was my fault, I must have passed some weakness on to Glen, it was all my fault.' Karina and I talked about this and she too had feelings of guilt. We were looking for ways to place the blame with something else, instead of facing up to the difficult task of accepting that it was a one in a million chance that this happened to our baby.

The morning of the funeral was so painful. Today we would lay our son to rest, the baby who was to have added so much more joy to our lives, but whose absence now brought pain and sorrow. Until that morning I had felt that I had done very well in holding myself together, but now after four cigarettes, I still couldn't come to my senses. I remember sitting on the edge of the bath thinking how unfair it all was.

The one thought that never crossed my mind was 'How could God let this happen?' I accepted that it was an act of nature and I could not blame God. The mourning car arrived and took us to the mortuary where members of the family were waiting. We formed a circle around Glen's coffin whilst prayers were said. Karina broke down and was inconsolable. We left then to go to the cemetery. We sat in the back of the car with our baby's tiny white coffin across our laps. It was the worst experience I have ever had. We sat there weeping, our hands joined and resting on the tiny coffin. Entering the cemetery, I saw my friend Ger standing with members of Karina's family. The car waited at the gate for a gravedigger to lead the way to Glen's final resting place.

Slowly he walked in front of the car with a shovel held horizontally across his right shoulder. Just another day, another funeral for him, I thought to myself. The car stopped and I inhaled deeply as Karina began to wail. Stepping from the car, I realised how light the coffin was, such a tiny being inside. The gravedigger who had led, his back to us, on that long journey, now reached to me for Glen. I hesitated, Karina wailed louder. I looked into the gravedigger's worn, weather-beaten face, and although for him it was just another funeral, there was compassion in his eyes. Taking hold of the coffin, he lowered his head slightly as if to acknowledge our sorrow. We stood there shattered, the prayers were over and it was time to go. Looking down we could see how small the coffin really was, a tiny body in a tiny coffin, in such a dark and lonely place. I carried Karina into the car, and on the way home I wrote the lines, 'I can't believe how I felt today, as we laid our child beneath the clay,/A time to part, a farewell touch, our little Glen to God we trust.'

At home we sat and drank tea. I noticed my mother-in-law, who had been so kind and supportive throughout this horrible time, had been crying. It was only then that I realised she had lost someone too.

In the afternoon my mood changed from sorrow to a burning rage. I was weary standing, uncomfortable sitting and too restless to lie down. Karina sat and stared into space; from time to time she would just break down and sob. I wanted to cry so much but I couldn't. I was so angry but I couldn't quite explain why or who I was angry with: myself, Karina, the doctors, God, Glen? Is it conceivable that I was angry at my son for dying? How incredible a notion! I felt so angry, I had to control myself in front of Karina, in fear of breaking something.

During the next few weeks I tried my best to get through each day. I tried to keep busy and finished 'Glen's Song'. I have only ever played it twice. Some weeks after the funeral, we went to see our doctor to discuss the post-mortem. We also joined in a therapy group for bereaved parents led by the social worker and chaplain from the hospital. This helped as we were able to talk to other people who had been in our situation and share experiences.

It took a long time to feel even semi-normal again. I remember some weeks after the funeral, I went into a pub in the middle of the afternoon on my own. As I was explaining about Glen to a barman, another customer was laughing loudly, at what I don't know – he was out of earshot. I felt so angry because he was laughing and I wanted to punch him. What did he think was so funny? My son had died and he was laughing. In time I learned that you can't blame the whole world for your troubles. Life must go on and you must learn to live with it.

Glen's death was a tragic loss; Karina and I suffered dearly. But in ways it has taught us to value life. There have been times when we have been over-protective with Karl, and now Sarah. Our baby's death brought the heavy burden of grief into our lives, and from that I have learnt that one cannot tell someone how to grieve, there are no rules and there is no code of rational thinking. For example, some people found it disturbing that I should write a song about my son's death: what did it gain? I don't know what it gained, but it helped me through it. When I talk of stillbirth, I mention Glen as a person, not something that never was, but as a baby, a tiny angel who never made it into this world, but who lives forever in our hearts.

Two years after Glen's birth, almost to the day, Sarah, our daughter was born. She brought a great deal of much-needed joy into our lives. She is perfect and everything we could wish for, but having said that, she is not Glen. Glen was Glen and Sarah is Sarah. Nobody could ever replace Glen, our son.

# Don't forget the children

The death of a baby affects every member of the family and children are no exception. Sometimes with the shock and sadness the needs and fears of the other children can be forgotten. It is very important during this traumatic time to remember that you have other children and you must try not to forget this.

A young child watches as the mother's stomach grows larger and listens intently to the reasons why. Everyone talks about how exciting it will be having a new baby. The parents prepare the child for the baby's arrival and for Mummy going into hospital and for visits to her and the new sister or brother. The child sees that everybody is happy because there is going to be a new baby and watches preparations being made for when the baby comes home. The child begins to realise that very soon there is going to be someone else, that he or she is not going to be the baby any more. Perhaps the child begins to worry that Mummy and Daddy won't love him or her anymore, and thinks about having to share the toys, and that maybe the baby isn't such a good idea after all.

On the other hand, the child may be looking forward to the arrival of the baby with great excitement, thinking about all the things they will be able to do together, about all the toys to show the new baby: there will be a new friend, a playmate. The child may begin to think of this baby as being his or her baby. In any event, the other children in the family will have very definite feelings about the arrival of the new baby and about the events leading up to it.

In all the discussions and explanations about the baby, there is rarely any question about whether or not the new arrival will be healthy. Death is not normally discussed because the parents themselves rarely expect it, it is something that probably is not even considered. Most couples take for granted that at the end of the nine months a healthy baby will be part of the family.

Trying to explain to a young child that the baby in Mummy's tummy won't be coming home is very difficult. When the child learns that the baby has died he or she may experience a vast array of emotions or perhaps just one or two. A young child will be confused, frightened and full of questions. Some children think that they are to blame because they didn't really want the baby, others believe that Mummy and Daddy told them lies about the new baby. Some children are angry at their parents: they were promised a new sister or brother and it died.

Children grieve in their own way; they often have the same feelings of anger, frustration and isolation as adults. This is sometimes expressed as bad behaviour. When speaking about death to a child keep it simple, direct and honest. Sometimes, because a child shows no outward signs of grief, it is assumed that they are too young to understand or that they have not been affected. This is not so. Children do grieve and need extra security throughout this traumatic time. It is important to reassure them that they were not in any way to blame and that they are not about to die.

Children must be included in the loss: if the death of their baby brother or sister is not spoken about or explained to them, then death becomes a taboo subject. They will become less inclined to ask questions and will keep their thoughts to themselves. This may result in needless worries and fears.

Regardless of the child's age, an explanation has to be given and his or her questions answered. Children of any age will sense that there is something wrong and will wonder why Mummy and Daddy are so sad. At first, parents may be too distraught to cope with their children's questions. Children are far more perceptive than we imagine and sometimes will be reluctant to express their thoughts in case they upset Mummy or Daddy even further. Not only have they suffered the loss of the new baby but also sometimes of their parents' attention in the first few overwhelming days of grief after the birth. The parents may not be able to give the children the emotional support they need during this time and this is when grandparents or close family friends can help. It is important that the child knows that there is someone to answer his or her questions.

It is a good idea, if the child is of school age, to inform the teacher about what has happened. That way, the teacher understands what the child is going through and can give support. Often a child will voice his or her fears or feelings of sadness to somebody outside the immediate family: a teacher may well be the person chosen.

Parents instinctively want to protect their children from pain and sorrow. However, excluding a child from the family experience may actually hinder the child from coming to terms with what has happened and with the whole concept of death.

The decision as to whether or not older children, in particular, should see the dead baby should be left up to them. Some children may want to see the baby, others may prefer not to. A child should never be forced to see a baby who has died. Like most adults, children have no idea what a dead baby looks like. Very often, they conjure up some nightmarish image in their mind. It is helpful, before any decision is taken, to show the child a photograph of the baby. This may be sufficient for the child: he or she will then have seen the baby. On the other hand it may allay any fears the child has of seeing the baby in reality. If, however, the baby is severely malformed, I personally feel that there is absolutely no advantage in the child seeing the baby.

Another thing that must be considered, one which I personally have not come across in my research, is that one day most of the brothers or sisters of the baby who died will come to have a baby themselves. Children who are old enough to understand what is happening when their baby sister or brother dies will be old enough to retain the memories of that time into adulthood. This is another reason why it is so important that a child understands what has happened as soon as possible after the baby is born.

It is generally accepted that children under the age of five have very little understanding about the finality of death and think of it as akin to a long sleep. My son, Karl, who was two and a half when Glen was stillborn, understood that Glen wouldn't be coming home. Karl is six and a half now and still asks questions about Glen. Recently, he was asked to draw a family tree in school and prominently displayed was 'my brother, Glen'. He often talks about his brother and then explains that Glen died. Karl sometimes looks up at the sky and says 'Look, Mummy, there's baby Glen's star.'

Children from the age of five to nine are more aware of death but only insofar as it is something that happens to other people. From the age of nine children know that at some time everybody is going to die and begin to ask questions about to their own mortality.

Every child will have questions about what has happened. It is important that these questions are encouraged and answered as honestly and simply as possible. If a child does not ask questions, then the subject should be broached gently and discussed. Questions may not have been asked because the child feels that the baby's death is a taboo subject, or because of fear of upsetting Mummy and Daddy. Remember, every child will have questions but those questions may not be voiced.

Even during the darkest hour, try and remember that you have other children and that they are probably just as upset as you are. Their upset is made far worse if they feel that their parents are not available to them: what they need above all is the security of their parents' love.

At what is a very difficult and traumatic time in their lives, you have to be there for your other children. Reassure them and help them to come to terms with and understand what has happened and why. Try not to become so overwhelmed with grief that your other children are pushed aside. At this time, more than ever, children need the reassurance of their parents. I myself was so overwhelmed with grief I lost interest in living. Three weeks after Glen's funeral, Karl asked me why I didn't love him any more. I couldn't believe that he had said this. In that instant I realised that Karl was still here and I had to start thinking about him. I took him in my arms and told him how sorry I was and we talked about Glen. This is why I want to stress how important it is to remember your other children and what they are going through.

# Grandparents – the hidden grief

When a pregnancy ends in miscarriage or stillbirth many members of the family are affected. It is easy to forget that grandparents grieve too. What must be remembered is that, not only are they agonising over the loss of their grandchild, but they are also having to watch their own child suffering without being able to ease their pain. They have a double loss: their dreams have been shattered and so have the dreams of their child.

It is a time when many different feelings surface. Grandparents may be surprised by some of the things they feel and shocked by the intensity of their feelings. It is important to realise that all of these feelings are quite normal and are part of the grieving process.

Anger can be directed at many people. For a short time one woman blamed her son-in-law. She had always loved him, but when she saw her daughter in so much pain and so distraught, she felt so helpless and so guilty that she directed her anger at him. After a couple of days she realised that this was not the answer and admitted to herself that it was nobody's fault and that it wasn't fair to blame anyone.

Another grandmother directed her anger at the baby. She had been looking forward eagerly to the birth, and when it was discovered that the baby would be stillborn for an instant she hated the baby. She blamed the baby for the pain and suffering it was causing her son and his wife. She was horrified that she had had such a thought.

A grandfather I spoke to directed his anger at the doctor. As he waited for his daughter to deliver his stillborn grandchild, he verbally abused the doctor, calling him incompetent. He later apologised for his outburst but was told there was no need to apologise, the doctor understood his grief.

Many parents feel responsible for their children and have a compelling urge to protect them. They feel guilty when they have to stand by and watch their child suffer, unable to do anything to prevent it. Other parents worry about whether or not they are saying or doing the right thing. Others simply question whether they were to blame in any way, whether the miscarriage or stillbirth came from 'my side of the family'. Many wish that they could change places with their child and spare them the suffering. They feel guilty because they themselves have never been in this situation. Others feel guilty for questioning God's will.

Very often grandparents are afraid to show emotion for fear of upsetting their child. They remain stoical and calm, feeling that they must be strong for their child. They think that if they are seen to be upset or in pain they won't be asked for help. However, hiding feelings of grief and loss may mean that the traumatic event is not discussed openly and honestly as a family. Suppressing the grief could also give the impression that the death doesn't warrant feelings of grief.

It is best to speak openly, to talk to the parents and outwardly show grief. This will benefit not only the parents of the baby, but also the grandparents themselves. It will give them a time to grieve openly with their child, for the baby that they have all lost. If a major trauma such as this is shared, it can make the grieving process a little easier and also bring the family closer together.

Grandparents should not be afraid to grieve openly. If there is a time when they feel like crying, they should go ahead and cry. They should talk about how they feel and their sense of loss to the parents. Initially, in the very early days after the birth and funeral, the grandparents' support will be needed and they will have to be strong and help their child. But their strength will not be determined by the fact that 'You didn't cry once' or 'Not once did you remind them or talk about the baby'. Their strength is determined by just being there for the parents and helping in any way they can.

Very often it is just help with the everyday things that is most needed and most appreciated. Whether it's cooking dinner or doing the washing, it helps. What also helps is to be there to listen. Very often parents will just want to talk and talk about what has happened, what the baby looked like, how they feel and about their despair. Grandparents should take their cue from them and tell them that they, too, have all these feelings and that they are not alone. They should cry with them, grieve with them and talk with them, and together as a family try to come to terms with their loss; a part of the grandparents, too, died when the baby died.

Parents who have lost a baby want people to acknowledge their loss. They do not want to look at their mother or father going about their business as if nothing has happened. This will only cause them to wonder if they really care about what has happened and whether or not they are grieving. It is best to be open, be honest and be there. If they do this the family will be united in grief and will share a better understanding of each other. Showing emotion and sharing grief will help greatly.

When Glen died I turned to my mother for support, and she was there for me twenty-four hours a day. It is only now that I realise that she, too, was grieving and had nobody to turn to. She had to put her feelings of grief and loss to one side and give me her undivided attention, putting on a brave face to do so. Her grief was something I had never really considered. She tells her story in the next chapter.

# A grandmother's story

Bouncing into the house one day, with the corners of his mouth tipping each ear, my son-in-law, Gerry, held out clenched fists, eagerly asking me to 'Pick one'. I did, and there, not even filling his outstretched palm, were two tiny socks, one pink, one blue. This is how I discovered that I had another grandchild on the way. Hot on his heels came my daughter, Karina, beaming, blooming and so very, very happy.

When Karina was about four and a half months pregnant she came home and announced that she had had a scan and the baby was fine and everything was going well. At this stage baby's big brother was looking forward to his future role and promised to share his toys with HIS new baby.

Well, in the time honoured and traditional role of grandmothers everywhere, out came the knitting needles and crochet hooks. With the determination that any grandchild of mine was going to start off dressed in fine clothes made with lots of love and soft wool, I set to knitting with gusto.

At about five and a half months, back pain – which Karina had suffered from for some time and during previous pregnancies – became unendurable. She was admitted to hospital for a few days to ease the pain. On the morning of her discharge, as a matter of routine, a scan was taken. Later that afternoon, I answered the phone to a very worried and tearful daughter who explained that the doctor wanted to see her and her husband together later that day.

At this stage my main concern was for Karina who was so worried that there was something wrong with the baby. I tried to reassure her and advised her to rest until Gerry and I arrived. I prayed that the news would not be too bad. I sat with them as the doctor, with the utmost kindness and honesty, told them that their little baby was dying and that the chances of anything other than a stillbirth were, in her opinion, zero.

I have to admit that, in previous miscarriages, my main, if not sole, concern was for Karina. This time though, my heart was breaking for all three of them.

I went home that night, and as I looked at the half-finished jackets, bootees and hats, I knew in my heart that they would not now be worn. In tears, I gathered them all up and put them away – I never wanted to see them again.

A couple of weeks later, a further scan revealed that the baby had died. It would be another two harrowing weeks before Karina finally gave 'birth'. I was already grieving for the grandchild I had so looked forward to, but my daughter's pain during this time can only be guessed at.

In due course I left Karina and Gerry to the hospital for what was to be a very quick and utterly sad birth. As I waited outside the labour ward, a nurse came out carrying a little white bundle. I asked her if that was the baby, to which she replied, 'Yes, would you like to see him?' I declined as I wanted to see him first with Karina or Gerry.

The nurse then proceeded to place the baby in what appeared to be a linen closet. As I sat opposite this door, which was ajar, another nurse came along to fetch or return linen. As she did so she noticed my grandson, who had been placed on what seemed to be some sort of scales, and went to look at him. On leaving the room she noticed another nurse passing, called her over and they both went back to look at him. When they had finished gaping, they went about their business. For some reason that hurt me and it still does. I felt that – unreasonable as it may be – he had been stripped of his dignity.

A few minutes later Gerry went into the linen room in tears and I listened as he sang a song to his son. A little while later, he called me into the room and handed my grandson to me, wrapped in white cotton wool. He then went to comfort Karina. As I gazed at my darling grandson's face, I could see how much he resembled his daddy. How different this was to how it should have been! Despite my grief, I was glad to have had the chance, if only for a few moments, to hold my little grandson in my arms and hope that, somehow, he knew how very, very much his grandma loved him.

I then had the difficult task of facing Karina who hadn't yet seen him. It was so hard to see my daughter's grief and to be powerless to prevent it. All I could do was to be there for her and for Gerry.

The next day I went to the mortuary where my grandson had been laid to rest. He was in a little Moses basket which was lined with blue satin. He was covered with a white blanket and a fresh yellow flower had been placed against his cheek. The kindness and solemnity of the mortuary attendant showed that he, too, was touched, however briefly, by the death of a very real little person. This meant so much.

On the eve of Glen's funeral, I did the only thing I would ever get a chance to do for him . . . With a very heavy heart, and so many tears that at times I could barely see what I was doing, but also with a great sense of privilege, I made him the tiniest, most beautiful white satin gown and bonnet for his burial the next day. His funeral was something that I never thought I would have to face.

In the weeks and months following the funeral, I tried to be strong for Karina but also grieved for the grandchild I had lost. Silently I prayed each night that some day my daughter and son-in-law would walk out of the hospital carrying a new baby in their arms. My prayers were answered when, two years and one day after my little grandchild died, Karina gave birth to a healthy baby girl. I will always remember my grandson and his little face will forever be etched on my mind. He is and always will be a very special memory.

# Before the funeral: decisions to make

In the hours and days following a stillbirth, at any stage of gestation, parents, shocked and grief-stricken as they are, have to make a number of important decisions concerning the baby. Sadly, in this situation, there are no second chances. With so much emotion and fatigue, and so little time before you must say goodbye to your baby, it is hard to make decisions and to think of all that you might like to do.

In this chapter I have outlined some of the decisions that will have to be made and given a list of things you might like to do before saying goodbye. Trained and sympathetic hospital staff will be on hand with support and counsel to help you: you will not be alone.

## Decisions to make
*1. Should I see the baby?*
There is no easy answer to this question; it is a decision only you can make. However, I would strongly recommend that you do see and hold your baby. If you decide initially not to see the baby do discuss your decision with a senior member of the hospital staff. I myself opted to see and hold my son; it gave me the opportunity to see his face and to create a lasting memory.

It is a good idea to ask somebody to take a photograph of your baby. In fact, it is standard practice now for hospitals to take pictures and keep them in case parents request a photograph at a later stage. Weeks, months, or even years after the birth there may come an overwhelming desire to know what the baby looked like.

*2. Should I name the baby?*

The simple answer to this question is 'Yes'. A name gives your baby an identity, recognised by all who come into contact with you and your infant. If you did not pick a name before the birth, do so when the baby is born. Then call the baby by the name you have chosen and tell the staff the name. While important at the time, it will be even more important in the future when you talk about the baby

In the family the baby will always be known by his or her name and not as 'the baby that died'. It is easier to talk about a named baby, whose memory is named. If you have a photograph on display, you can refer to your baby by name.

When other children are aware of the baby's existence, and subsequent death, it is important to be able to talk about the baby, who is, after all, their brother or sister and a part of their family, by name. The baby's name can be put on a headstone on the grave or on a plaque in the garden of rembrance.

This baby's name should not be used for another baby. The baby you have lost can never be replaced. His or her memory will live on through you, and to give that name to another baby would not be fair either to the memory of the baby you lost or to the new baby; it would be a constant reminder of what might have been.

From the moment our stillborn baby was born, he was called 'Glen', and any time anyone spoke about him, he was referred to by name. He was a baby, a human being and we wanted him to be known as Glen and not as 'The Stillbirth' or 'Baby X'. He was a very real person to us and we wanted those who came into contact with him to know his name and to use it when speaking about him. When the nurses or doctors spoke about Glen by name, to us it was a recognition of him as a very real person. This was very, very important to us. He was never dismissed as 'just' a stillbirth.

There would be no question about naming a healthy new-born: equally, there should be no question about naming a stillborn baby. It is a baby, your baby, to be named with love.

*3. Should I consent to an autopsy?*
Soon after the birth, the parents will be asked if they will consent to an autopsy being performed on the baby to try to discover the cause of death; permission from a parent must be obtained. Most parents are anxious to know why their baby died and agree to an autopsy. However, sometimes little is discovered from an autopsy so it is important to realise this. Some parents refuse permission because they feel their baby has gone through enough.

In my case, my husband and I had discussed the question of an autopsy before the birth and agreed that we would give our permission. We felt that we might learn more about why our baby died. We also felt that something might be found that would prove valuable to research; if it would help even one other baby, then Glen's death would not have been in vain. I gave my permission without hesitation and chose not to think about what an autopsy entailed. It was a decision I do not regret, and a couple of months later we went to see our doctor and discussed the findings of the autopsy in depth, which helped us both understand why Glen had died. Again this is a decision that only the individuals concerned can make.

### 4. How will I say 'Goodbye'?

There is no answer to this question. It is the most heartbreaking thing for any parent to have to do. It will seem like only minutes since the birth, and in most cases will be only a day or two later. It is a very short period of time in which to adjust from seeing the baby to saying goodbye. The hardest thing to accept is the fact this is such a final goodbye.

I would suggest that you agree a time, and when that time comes prepare yourself for a final farewell and accept that it is the last time you will see the baby. This is the time to make sure that you are satisfied you have done and said everything. As you bend to kiss or touch your baby for one last time, find solace in the fact that your child did not suffer and is now at peace.

### 5. What funeral arrangements should I make?

There are a number of funeral options to choose from. There is no one 'right' choice – the final decision can only be made by the parents.

Some of the options that are available are:
- Buying a new family grave: with the unexpected death of a baby, parents sometimes make the decision to purchase a family grave at a graveyard of their choosing.
- Using an existing family grave: sometimes parents prefer to have the baby buried alongside grandparents or other relatives. It is necessary to get permission from the family to do this.
- Cremation: It is important that you let the hospital and undertaker know of your decision so that arrangements can be made.
- Hospital burial: parents unable to consider any of the options above or who can't cope with funeral arrangements, can ask the hospital to make the arrangements. In this situation, the baby is buried in

one of the graves designated for babies who die around the time of birth. Most parents attend the funeral; some decide not to attend.

*6. Should I ask for counselling?*
Don't be afraid to ask for counselling if you think you would benefit from it. Counselling is not just for people who are finding it hard to cope. It is also intended to help anybody going through a crisis, who needs reassurance that what they are feeling is normal, and who would be helped by the opportunity to express their feelings and thoughts in a 'safe' place. It helps people to make sense of what has happened so that they can, in due course, pick up the threads of their lives again.

One of the most difficult times is after you go home. If you contact the sister in the hospital where the baby was born she will arrange support for you. Most maternity hospitals and departments offer counselling support to bereaved parents.

I now know that counselling would have helped me to come to terms with Glen's death and would have given me the reassurance that what I was feeling and going through was normal. It would also have given me the opportunity to talk about how I was really feeling openly and honestly without having to hide my true feelings.

**Things you may wish to do**
After the birth of their stillborn baby, parents are anxious to spend what little time they have holding and talking to their baby. It is easy to forget to take keepsakes, or to do something that later might give you comfort, little things that will eliminate the regret of 'Why didn't I think of doing that?'

This list will remind you of things you may wish to do.

1. Take photographs of the baby. Ask someone to photograph you and your partner, if you have one, with the baby.
2. Take the baby's hand and footprints: most maternity hospitals offer this service, but if not it is quite easy to do with an ink pad (available from stationers) and a piece of white card.
3. If the baby has hair, cut a lock to keep.
4. Ask the hospital staff for your baby's weight and measurements.
5. Ask the hospital staff for photographs of any scans that were done of your baby.
6. If you consent to an autopsy ask for a copy of the report.
7. Ask the hospital staff for your baby's identification bracelet.
8. Some parents may wish to ask their clergyman about a 'Remembrance Blessing'.
9. Arrange a time for members of the family to say goodbye to the baby.
10. Decide on the clothes that you would like to dress the baby in.
11. Have you thought of anything that you would like to put in the coffin? For example, a letter or a family photograph. If you have another child or children they may like to choose a toy or a drawing to give to their little brother or sister.
12. Decide whether to put a notice in the newspaper.
13. If you have other children, think about whether to bring them to see the baby. They may wish to put their toy or other little gift in the coffin themselves.
14. During your stay in hospital, ask to see your baby as often as you wish. Spend as much time as you want with the baby.

15. If you and/or your partner want time alone with your baby, express this wish to the staff.
16. Finally, when the time comes for you to say a final goodbye to your baby, make sure that you are happy you have done everything you wanted to do.

## Further reading

ISANDS *A Little Lifetime* Irish Stillbirth & Neonatal Death Society, Dublin

Colin Murray Parkes *Bereavement* (1980) Pelican, Harmondsworth

Hank Pizer & Christine O'Brien Palinski *Coping with a Miscarriage* (1981) Jim Norman Ltd., New York

Ann Byrne-Lynch & Martine Millet *Miscarriage* (1990) South Eastern Health Board, Kilkenny

Wendy Jones *Miscarriage* (1990) Thorsons, Wellingborough

Margaret Leroy *Miscarriage* (1988) Optima, London

Christine Moulder *Miscarriage* (1990) Pandora Press, London

Ann Oakley, Ann McPherson & Helen Roberts *Miscarriage* (1990) Penguin, Harmondsworth

Larry Peppers & Ronald Knapp *Motherhood and Mourning* (1980) Praegar, New York

Bonnie Glastin & Rochelle Friedman *Surviving Pregnancy Loss* (1992) Little, Brown, London

Sarah Murphy *Talking About Miscarriage* (1992) Sheldon Press, London

Alix Henley & Nancy Kohner *When a Baby Dies* (1991) Pandora Press, London

**For children:**

Siobhán Parkinson *All Shining When the Spring Comes* (1994) O'Brien Press, Dublin

## Useful addresses

The Irish Stillbirth and Neonatal Death Society, Carmichael House, North Brunswick St., Dublin 7. Telephone 01-2831910/2809163/8373367. Contact list of telephone numbers in other parts of Ireland available.

The Miscarriage Association of Ireland, 27 Kenilworth Road, Dublin 6. Telephone 01-972938. Contact list of telephone numbers in other parts of Ireland available.